WELSH LANDFORMS
AND SCENERY

BY

G. MELVYN HOWE, M.Sc., Ph.D.
Reader in Geography
University College of Wales, Aberystwyth

AND

PETER THOMAS, B.Sc.
Formerly Senior Geography Master
Ysgol Sir Ffestiniog, Blaenau Ffestiniog

LONDON
MACMILLAN & CO LTD
NEW YORK · ST MARTIN'S PRESS
1965

MACMILLAN AND COMPANY LIMITED
Little Essex Street London WC2
also Bombay Calcutta Madras Melbourne

THE MACMILLAN COMPANY OF CANADA LIMITED
70 Bond Street Toronto 2

ST MARTIN'S PRESS INC
175 Fifth Avenue New York 10010 NY

PRINTED IN GREAT BRITAIN

PREFACE

THE contortions, distortions, sculpturing and moulding of rocks representing practically every period in geological time have provided Wales with an endless variety of scenery rarely surpassed in a country of comparable size. Students have undertaken valuable studies on the various aspects of the Welsh landscape and many of the original ideas connected with the concept of the cycle of erosion as presented by the eminent American geomorphologist, W. M. Davis, were based on observations made in Wales; but at no time have the oft-quoted classical examples of the many landforms studied been presented in a single volume. The present study is an attempt to rectify this situation for some of the more common landforms.

The landforms have been grouped into the following categories: tectonic, igneous and gradational, to facilitate systematic treatment. But since no landform can be defined or classified on the basis of a single set of factors or processes, repetition of certain features is inevitable. Cross-referencing is frequent and, naturally, desirable if a reasonably comprehensive explanation of the mode of formation of a particular feature is to be presented.

Illustrations in the form of photographs, block diagrams, maps and sketches, have been used to depict the selected landforms. Each specific example is described and, where possible, explained. For the benefit of all lovers of the countryside and for students anxious to examine similar landform features elsewhere in Wales, other examples, located by the sheet number of the relevant Seventh Series Ordnance Survey One-inch map and National Grid references, are listed. For example, the cirque Ffynnon Lloer '(107, 6662)' means Sheet 107, Grid Reference 6662. A four-figure Grid Reference represents the grid square and six figures the precise reference to within 100 metres. A list of sheet numbers and the names of one-inch Ordnance Survey maps covering Wales is given in Appendix I.

The spellings of *Welsh* place- and feature-names throughout the book are in accordance with those given in *A Gazetteer of Welsh Place Names*, edited by Dr. Elwyn Davies, Cardiff, 1957. Where, however, the more familiar forms are English, or highly anglicised,

v

these have been retained. For instance, 'Dolgellau', being a name of Welsh origin, is spelt accordingly, but in the case of 'Cardiff' (Caerdydd), the more familiar anglicised form is adopted.

The authors wish to acknowledge the kindness of the following in giving permission for the use of photographs:

Geological Survey (Figs. 3, 12, 26, 34, 48, 58, 79, 84, 105, 106, 108) ; H. Tempest Ltd. (Figs. 41, 60, 61, 72, 89, 92, 101, 109) ; University of Cambridge Committee for Aerial Photography (Figs. 50, 57, 96) ; Air Ministry (Crown Copyright Reserved, photographs by J. K. St. Joseph, Figs. 7, 14, 111, 113) ; Air Ministry (Crown Copyright Reserved, R.A.F. photographs, Figs. 38, 63, 66) ; G. P. Abraham, Ltd. (Figs. 19, 70) ; J. Challinor (Figs. 103, 104) ; R. Forrester-Addie (Fig. 24) ; D. W. Thomas (Fig. 39) ; M. L. Davies (Fig. 110) ; W. A. Evans (Fig. 102) ; R. Gethin (Figs. 64, 65) ; S. G. Brown (Fig. 35) ; F. Frith & Co. Ltd. (Fig. 44) ; Aerofilms & Aero Pictorial, Ltd. (Fig. 36) ; M. C. Morgan (Fig. 82) ; J. G. Jones (Fig. 47).

All other photographs were taken by the authors specially for this book. The authors are also indebted to Dr. Eric Brown and the University of Wales Press for information contained in Figs. 2, 52, 97, 98 and 100 (taken from *The Relief and Drainage of Wales*) and to T. M. Thomas for the loan of the block for Fig. 66 (taken from the *Geomorphology of Brecknock, Brycheiniog*, vol. 5, 1959). Figs. 78 and 88 are based on the respective one-inch Ordnance Survey maps, with the sanction of the Controller of H.M. Stationery Office.

They wish to thank Mr. J. Challinor and other colleagues in the University College of Wales, Aberystwyth, for reading through the draft manuscript and making several useful observations. Where questions of interpretation are in doubt, the authors and not the above are responsible for opinions presented. Finally, they wish to express their appreciation to Mr. Vincent F. Seabourne for his artist's impression (Fig. 43), of the work of Mr. David Griffiths, who prepared many of the diagrams and other illustrations from drafts supplied by the authors, thereby adding considerably to the general presentation of the work, and to Mr. George Davies for his two line-drawings (Figs. 22 and 74).

CONTENTS

LIST OF ILLUSTRATIONS

INTRODUCTION

'THE rocks and their contents form one subject of study, the history of their present scenery forms another.' So wrote Sir Archibald Geikie in his book *A Text Book of Geology*, the fourth and last edition of which was published in 1903. Here was drawn one of the earliest distinctions between Geology and Geomorphology respectively. It was W. M. Davis, the famous American geomorphologist and contemporary of Geikie, who first marshalled the academic discipline of the subject, and it was he also who first introduced the idea of the Cycle of Erosion which is still a fundamental principle in Geomorphology. Davis' idea of this academic discipline was that each landform is a function of a structure, a process and a stage. It is this idea which forms the basis of the present study.

Broadly speaking, one may recognise two groups of forces which interact to produce landforms. First, there is a group which originates mainly from within the earth's crust and which tends to produce differences in elevation on the earth's surface. This group, called the *tectonic* forces, includes faulting, folding and earth movements of all descriptions, and produces weaknesses in the earth's crust which are frequently exploited by subsequent *igneous* activity. These together may be regarded as accounting for Davis' *structure*. Second, however, these structural features are constantly being attacked by the *gradational* forces, whose broad purpose is to reduce the landscape to uniformity by erosion (degradation) of the higher parts, and deposition of the material so removed in the lowlands (aggradation). This latter group originates from outside the earth's crust, and, by means of weathering and the main denudational agents of running water, ice and wind, their tendency is to remove the crustal irregularities of altitude brought about by the tectonic forces. This second group may be taken as broadly analogous to Davis' *process*.

A landform is thus the product of a continuous interaction between the tectonic and the gradational processes. W. M. Davis would probably say that the gradational *process* acts upon the tectonic *structure* to produce the *stage*. Considering the enormous

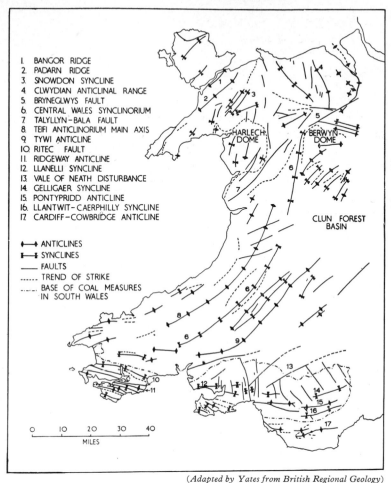

1. BANGOR RIDGE
2. PADARN RIDGE
3. SNOWDON SYNCLINE
4. CLWYDIAN ANTICLINAL RANGE
5. BRYNEGLWYS FAULT
6. CENTRAL WALES SYNCLINORIUM
7. TALYLLYN–BALA FAULT
8. TEIFI ANTICLINORIUM MAIN AXIS
9. TYWI ANTICLINE
10. RITEC FAULT
11. RIDGEWAY ANTICLINE
12. LLANELLI SYNCLINE
13. VALE OF NEATH DISTURBANCE
14. GELLIGAER SYNCLINE
15. PONTYPRIDD ANTICLINE
16. LLANTWIT–CAERPHILLY SYNCLINE
17. CARDIFF–COWBRIDGE ANTICLINE

ANTICLINES
SYNCLINES
FAULTS
TREND OF STRIKE
BASE OF COAL MEASURES
IN SOUTH WALES

HARLECH DOME
BERWYN DOME
CLUN FOREST BASIN

0   10   20   30   40
MILES

(*Adapted by Yates from British Regional Geology*)

FIG. I. Main structural elements of Wales.

strides which Geomorphology has made since 1900 these two viewpoints show a surprising consistency of outlook.

Applying these ideas to Wales, two principal lines of structural trend — represented in the dominant orientations of ridges, faults and the axes of anticlines and synclines — are immediately evident (Fig. 1). The Black Mountains, Mynydd Epynt, the Brecon Beacons, the Black Mountain, Mynydd Prescelly and the South

Wales Coalfield Plateau, all show the west–east Hercynian or Armorican trend; the structural connections are with Devon and Cornwall and Brittany. Northwards, the rest of the Welsh mountains show the dominant south-west–north-east Caledonian trend so typical of the Scottish Highlands, although the Vale of Clwyd (Dyffryn Clwyd) is a significant exception.

However, a study of the landscape variation of Wales in more detail reveals that this duality in structural trend is of less importance than the 'process' in producing the astonishing variety of landscapes to be found. And process itself varies with climate, which has changed markedly throughout geological time (Appendix III). During Devonian times, it was desert; during Pleistocene times, it was glacial. When the coal measures were formed during Carboniferous times, the climate must have been tropical or sub-tropical. The effects of ice have been of varying importance and character; moreover, the cycle of river erosion has been interrupted on numerous occasions by rejuvenation, and again, the intrusion of igneous rocks has produced features of outstanding relief. Finally, Wales' coastline, subjected as it has been to alternating periods of submergence and emergence with respect to sea-level, is one of outstanding beauty and variety of scenery.

It is the geomorphologist's task to classify and interpret this variety of landforms, and the main purpose of this book is to select the most characteristic Welsh landscape features, and to discuss their formation and appearance. In order that each landform may fall into correct regional perspective, the following simple classification of landscapes in Wales (Fig. 2) is offered:

1. *Uplands.*—Generally between about 750 feet and 3,500 feet.
   (a) *Severely glaciated uplands* like Snowdonia, the Migneint (including Arennig Fawr), Rhinog Fawr and the Cadair Idris Range. By virtue of their north-westerly locations and high relief (2,000–3,560 feet now, but higher in glacial times) these areas experienced heavy snowfall during the great Pleistocene Ice Age which caused them to be centres of severe valley glaciation. Cirques (corries), arêtes, glaciated valleys, hanging valleys, ribbon lakes and great near-vertical crags are found in profusion and serve to give these uplands great grandeur of scenery.
   (b) *Subdued uplands and plateaux* like the Denbighshire Moors,

the Clwydian Range, the Aran Range, Plynlimon Range, Radnor Forest, Mynydd Epynt, Black Mountains, Brecon Beacons, Black Mountain, Mynydd Prescelly and the South Wales Coalfield Plateau. These regions, while most were certainly glaciated to a marked degree (in particular the higher ranges of the Arans, Berwyns, Plynlimon, Brecon Beacons and the Black Mountains), do not show the striking results of glaciation in such profusion as do the regions of group (a). Cirques of classic form, for instance, have been developed only in some half-dozen locations, whereas in

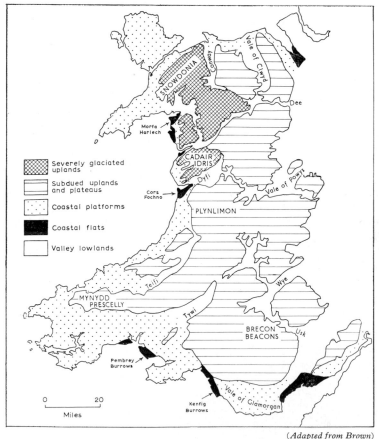

(*Adapted from Brown*)

FIG. 2.   Major landscape regions of Wales.

group (a) there are as many on the Snowdon Massif alone. Expanses of moorland are common, and the effects of river erosion have a much greater relative importance in the landscape. The long rectangular ribbon lakes which contribute so much to the attractions of Snowdonia are absent from counties other than Caernarvonshire and Merionethshire. The landforms, while often equally large and extensive, lack the severity and striking beauty of those of Snowdonia, and are consequently less frequented by tourists, except where there are special local attractions such as the reservoirs at Llyn Vyrnwy, Montgomeryshire, or the Elan Valley, Radnorshire. The beauty is more subdued, yet wilder.

Within both the severely glaciated and the more subdued types of upland can be included valleys such as Dyffryn Ogwen in North Wales or the coal-mining valleys of South Wales, which from the point of view of landforms are not large enough to be regarded as other than dissections of the main highland blocks of which they thus form part.

2. *Lowlands.*—Generally below 700 feet.
  (a) *Coastal platforms*, mainly peneplanes of marine erosion which have been uplifted to a moderate degree, forming plateaux usually 200–600 feet above sea-level. Into this category would come the Vale of Glamorgan, Gower, South Pembrokeshire, the Cardiganshire Coastal Plateau, much of Llŷn, the Plain of Arfon (Caernarvon–Bangor) and Anglesey. Subsequent erosion of rivers has often given entrenched valleys which, in some instances, *e.g.* West Cardiganshire, may facilitate communication, but in others, *e.g.* Vale of Glamorgan, may prove a great handicap to communications.
  (b) *Coastal flats*, nearly always below 50 feet, found in scattered locations and formed as a result of marine and stream deposition during Quaternary times.
  (c) *Valley lowlands*, variously referred to in Welsh as 'glyn (-noedd)', 'cwm (cymoedd)', 'dyffryn (-noedd)' and sometimes as 'bro (-ydd)', although the strict meaning of the last is 'district' rather than 'vale'. These vales are too large to be included as part of their surrounding highland blocks, and must be regarded as separate regions in their own right, both physically and culturally. Included here are the Vales of

B

Clwyd and Conway (Dyffryn Clwyd a Dyffryn Conwy), the Vale of Ffestiniog (Bro Ffestiniog), the Vales of Tegid and Edeirnion (Upper Dee valley), the Teifi Valley, the Tywi Valley and the vales of the rivers Usk, Wye, Severn (Powys) and Dee (Glyn Dyfrdwy) in the east.

Tectonic Features

TECTONIC features are the result of forces originating within the earth's crust, and tend to produce differences in surface elevation on it. No one will have failed to see the various contortions of the rocks in the exposed face of a quarry, sea-cliff (Fig. 3) or road-cutting. They may be in the form of gentle upfolds (anticlines) or downfolds (synclines), sometimes tilted up at sharp angles (Fig. 4), at others dislocated by faults and fractures (Fig. 5). Clearly, to have attained such a state, the rocks must have been subjected to intense pressures. At first the rocks (apart from crystalline ones) accumulated as marine sediments in layers (strata) below sea-level, the upper surface of any one of which was flat and almost horizontal. But whether they be sedimentary, like limestones, shales or sandstones, or crystalline (igneous), like granites, basalts, or gneisses which solidified from an originally molten material, it is obvious they must all have experienced very many vicissitudes.

FIG. 3.   Folded strata at South Stack, near Holyhead, Anglesey.

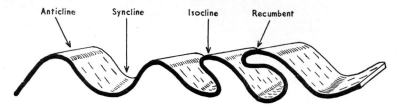

Anticline   Syncline   Isocline   Recumbent

FIG. 4.   Main types of folds.

Upward movements relative to sea-level originated dry land and exposed the land surface to gradational forces; downward movement relative to the sea subjected the land surface to the abrasive action of the sea and submarine platforms resulted.   Such *epeirogenetic* ('continent building') movements of uplift and depression took place during several well-marked periods throughout geological time (Appendix III), and in their turn they influenced the gradational processes.   Uplifts resulted in a speeding-up (rejuvenation) of river erosion, while downward movement resulted in a slackening of this activity, encouraging aggradation of previously eroded material and the drowning of river valleys.   Similar effects were produced respectively by *negative* and *positive* movements of sea-level, usually referred to as '*eustatic*' movements.

These changes in the relative elevation of land and sea took place gently and represented the local or world-wide maintenance of a state of balance within the earth's crust.   Distortions of the strata, on the other hand, did not result from simple uplift or subsidence. Horizontal (*orogenetic*) movements, resulting in lateral compression and tension and consequent rucking of the initially flat layers of rocks, must have taken place.   Compression leads to a folding of the earth's crust, sometimes a series of gentle upfolds and downfolds, at others, more complicated structures involving intense folding, over-thrusting and fracturing (Fig. 4).   Tension leads to stresses in the earth's crust and reveals itself locally as systems of joints in the rocks or regionally as great fractures or faults.   In the case of faults one block of land is displaced relative to another, usually in a vertical or steeply inclined plane (Fig. 5).

The foundation of what is now Wales was faulted, fractured and contorted by earth-movements before the dawn of the Cambrian Period, over five hundred million years ago.   But it was the Caledonian earth-movements at the close of the Silurian Period and the Hercynian (Armorican) earth-movements at the close of the

Carboniferous period (Appendix III) which were probably the most significant as far as the folding and fracturing of the later strata were concerned. Two great downfolds or synclines were developed during the Caledonian earth-movements, the Snowdon syncline and the Central Wales syncline. It was during this period, also, that the structural trend now followed by the subsequent valleys of Tal-y-llyn and Tegid (Bala) was laid down, although the present faults may be due to 'posthumous' movement during Tertiary times.

The old rocks of North Wales were not so much affected by the later Hercynian earth-movements, but in South Wales the rocks were folded into a great syncline with a west to east trend. The upturned strata along the northern and southern margins of this great basin now form pronounced escarpments, the Brecon Beacons and the Black Mountains in the north being the most striking. Much faulting took place, the Vale of Clwyd in north-east Wales being partly formed at this time, although later movements also contributed to its formation.

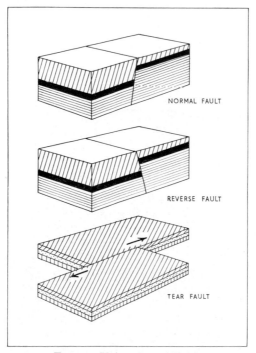

FIG. 5. Main types of faults.

Since many of the tectonic forces accomplished their work in Wales in distant geological times when the land surface was probably several hundreds of feet above its present level, it is obvious that the original constructional effects have, in many instances, been largely obliterated, or at least masked by the ravages of the age-long interplay between the original rock structures and the unending attack of denudation. The examples that follow represent features that were *initiated* by tectonic forces and are intended to illustrate the contribution of these forces to the building of the Welsh landscape. It is not intended to imply that tectonic forces were solely responsible for them; in fact it may well be that their influence is only indirect, as in the case of a fault-guided valley.

FAULT-GUIDED VALLEYS

Faults are cracks or fractures in the earth's crust on either side of which the rocks have been displaced, sometimes for as little as a fraction of an inch, at others for distances of several thousands of feet. Cracking of this kind usually proceeds slowly, though sudden collapsing may cause an earthquake. A *normal* fault is the result of tension in the earth's surface whereby the strata on one side have been let down or slip out of alignment, bringing dissimilar strata into close association. Sometimes, however, the fault is the result of extensive compression whereby the strata are pushed upwards along a thrust plane, thereby providing a *thrust* or reverse fault. At other times, dissimilar strata are brought into close association as a result of horizontal movement along a fault plane (Fig. 5).

In either case, the shattering of the rocks involved in immediate association with such faults provides belts of strata that are easily eroded and locally influence the development of valleys. Such a fault-influenced or fault-guided valley is the 10-mile cleft of Tal-y-llyn under Cadair Idris, Merioneth, where the strata on the south side of the fault have moved almost horizontally towards the east for a distance of about two miles. This lowland trough, cutting along the general Caledonian 'grain' and relief pattern of the area, is a most striking feature of the Welsh landscape. It represents part of line of earth tearing and shattering which stretches as an arc from near Towyn along the long narrow straight valley framing Tal-y-llyn,

FIG. 6. Tal-y-llyn valley, Merioneth, looking south-west, showing the straight alignment of the valley and the lower glaciated slopes of Cadair Idris (*right*) and Graig Goch (*left*).

over the low shoulder of the Cross Foxes (116, 766167) to the long, narrow Bala Lake. A branch or subordinate line of this deep cleft extends to Dolgellau and the Mawddach estuary. Beyond Bala to the north-east this structural lowland continues into both the upper Dee lowland and along the Bryneglwys Fault into the Vale of Clwyd. From the west coast to the north coast there is thus a narrow, arc-like strip of lowland, about 120 miles long, etched out by erosion along lines of structural weakness due to faulting. This effectively separates the upland blocks, Snowdonia-Arennigs-Rhinogs from the Cadair Idris-Aran-Berwyn group.

Fig. 6 shows the view south-west along the Tal-y-llyn trough from near Ty'n-y-maes (116, 734113), a point some 800 feet above sea-level. The remarkable straightness of the valley, aligned north-east to south-west, is the surface expression of the tear fault, the shattering effects of which provided a belt of strata along which the upper section of the present Dysynni river was able to erode quickly and easily. The present form of the valley and that of the enclosed lake bespeak of a glaciated upland. The U-shaped cross section, with an absence of interlocking spurs projecting from the valley side, the discordant or 'hanging' nature of the tributary streams, which descend to the main stream (River Dysynni) or the lake, partly as rapids and partly as waterfalls, and the lake itself are all features indicative of glacial scouring in a valley already in existence in pre-glacial times.   At their confluence with the main stream or with the lake the sudden checking of the tributary waters has resulted in the formation of small side-deltas and the building up of alluvial cones (right centre).   The lake is surprisingly shallow, being nowhere deeper than 12 feet. Its surface is 270 feet above O.D. The unusually steep slopes of the valley sides (in many cases exceeding 40°) are clearly visible.   Those on the north rise to a height of 2,927 feet at Pen-y-Gadair in the Cadair Idris Range, those

FIG. 7.   Aerial view of Tal-y-llyn–Tegid fault-guided valley looking north-east.   The trunk road A487 in the foreground links Machynlleth with Dolgellau *via* Cross Foxes (*left background*). Llyn Tegid is visible in the distance.

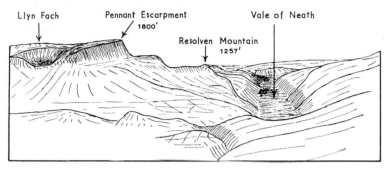

Llyn Fach   Pennant Escarpment   Vale of Neath
1800'

Resolven Mountain
1257'

FIG. 8. Vale of Neath, Glamorgan, looking south-west from A4086 north of Penderyn. The two settlements represented are Resolven and Neath (*distance*).

of Graig Goch on the south rise to a summit height of 1,882 feet The valley lake itself belongs to the ribbon lake category (p. 82), clearly occupying a rock basin, since the outlet is over a rock bar (Watson, 1960). The bar of material at the head of the lake, which has no bearing on the present water level, appears, at first sight, to be of morainic origin, but recent investigation (Watson, 1962) favours an interpretation based upon massive landslips from the face of Graig Goch (left centre).

Fig. 7 is an aerial view north-east from near Tal-y-llyn and shows the continuation of the fault-guided valley, followed by the A487 road, over the low shoulder at Cross Foxes and thence to Bala. Here, again, the valley is occupied by a lake into which a pronounced deltaic fan extends from the south bank (p. 43). The mountains visible along the south side of the valley are Mynydd Ceiswyn 1,983 feet (centre foreground), Maesglasau 2,111 feet, Aran Fawddwy 2,970 feet and Aran Benllyn 2,901 feet (centre background).

In South Wales, the straight, trench-like lowlands occupied by the Neath (Nedd) (Fig. 8) and Tawe rivers are further examples of fault-guided valleys. The rivers follow belts of compression and shatter which traverse the northern limb of the South Wales syncline. They are aligned mainly west/south-west–east/north-east and are, in consequence, at variance with the normal west-east Armorican 'trend' which is characteristic of other South Wales structures. Both valleys are now markedly flat-bottomed glaciated trenches, originally etched out by subsequent tributaries to older rivers along lines of disturbed strata. The development of these subsequent tributaries (*i.e.* the Neath and Tawe) was accompanied by extensive river capture involving, for example, capture of the headwaters of the River Cynon by the River Neath (p. 59).

RIFT VALLEYS

When the earth's crust is fractured or dislocated along two roughly parallel fault systems and the strip or block of country between either slips or is forced down, a trough or rift valley results. If the faulting is the result of horizontal tensional forces the depression is due to a general down-dropping of the land between; but if the forces are compressional in character, then the depression is the result of down-forcing of the intervening land along thrust or reverse faults (Fig. 9).

The great lowland trough of the Vale of Clwyd (Figs. 10 and 11) may be cited as a Welsh example of a rift valley though the relief of this now rich, smiling vale cannot be described as 'original' in the sense that it represents the straightforward collapsing of the earth's crust between two lines of fracturing or faulting. The Vale certainly has all the features of a miniature rift; its eastern boundary is a sharp fault-line scarp (p. 11) with a rather less-marked series of minor faults on the west, but its mode of formation and present surface form are far more complex. At first the Vale of Clwyd was

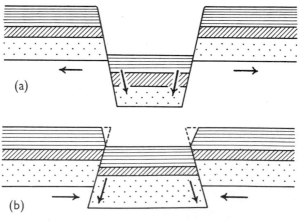

FIG. 9.   Diagrammatic sections across rift valleys.

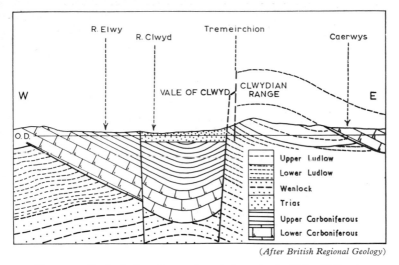

W R. Elwy R. Clwyd Tremeirchion Caerwys E

VALE OF CLWYD CLWYDIAN RANGE

O.D.

Upper Ludlow
Lower Ludlow
Wenlock
Trias
Upper Carboniferous
Lower Carboniferous

(After British Regional Geology)

FIG. 10. Geological section east-west through the Vale of Clwyd, north-east Wales.

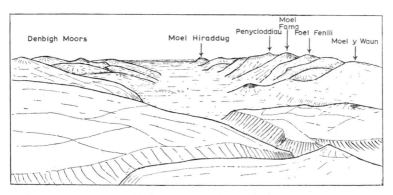

Denbigh Moors Moel Hiraddug Penycloddiau Moel Fama Foel Fenlli Moel y Waun

FIG. 11. Vale of Clwyd looking northwards.

represented by a deep, faulted syncline formed as a result of great earth movements that took place at the close of the Carboniferous epoch. On the tilted and denuded remnants of this original structure were spread New Red Sandstone deposits which in their turn were eventually let down along the lines of the old fractures to form a faulted trough overlying the existing faulted syncline. River erosion and glacial action within the low-lying intervening tract have since contributed to the present 'secondary' character of the Vale (Fig. 10).

Nevertheless, while the relief is not strictly 'original', the Vale certainly was, in the first instance, a tectonic feature and is truly a piece of the Midland Plain which has been, so to speak, 'dropped' amidst the Welsh Uplands, for within the trough are preserved soft Triassic rocks bounded by older and harder rocks of Silurian and Carboniferous age.

In South Wales a 'secondary' rift valley is represented by the Dyffryn trough which links the town of Neath with Cilybebyll. Here, between Mynydd March-Hywel (153, 7603, 1,350 feet) in the east and Mynydd Drumau (7200, 893 feet) in the west are preserved soft Upper Coal Series strata which were let down between the Rhydding and Dyffryn Faults. The actual physiographic trough as it exists at the present time is not, it should be emphasised, the direct result of recent depression of the land between the two faults, but of age-long river and glacial erosion acting upon hard and soft strata.

It sometimes happens that younger rocks which collapse between faults are more resistant to erosion than are the rocks which are left upstanding. In this case, erosion will eventually wear away the softer rocks and leave the resistant rocks standing out as a hill or outlier. The crag on which stands Carreg Cennen Castle (140, 6619), in Carmarthenshire, is a good Welsh example of such a feature (Fig. 12). The castle is built on an outlier of Carboniferous Limestone, which

FIG. 12.   Castell Carreg Cennen, Carmarthenshire.

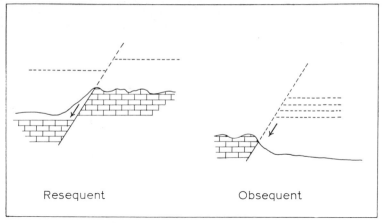

Resequent   Obsequent

Fig. 13.   Fault-line escarpments.

was initially let down in the midst of Old Red Sandstone country by
an eastward continuation of the Llandyfaelog belt of faulting.   The
southern face of the crag is a fault scarp, while a fault also bounds
the northern side.   The actual castle, originally a Welsh native
fortress, changed hands five times during the decade following 1277
before being finally reconstructed by the Normans.

FAULT-LINE ESCARPMENTS

The surface of the land of Wales has been so modified by erosion
that it is now several hundreds of feet below the level at which most of
the original (Caledonian or Hercynian) faulting and fracturing took
place.   Nevertheless, the fact that these crustal movements often
brought rocks of differing degrees of resistance together means that,
even to this day, irregularities in the landscape continue to follow
the lines of fracturing or faulting.   In cases where softer rocks were
brought into juxtaposition with harder rocks the less resistant rocks
form the lower ground while the resistant rocks stand out above as
so-called fault-line escarpments (Fig. 13).

The pronounced fault-line scarp marking the eastern boundary
of the Clwyd valley has already been noted (p. 8), but the western
boundary of the near-by Conway valley in the vicinity of Dolgarrog is
an equally good example of this landform.   In this flat, cultivated

north-south stretch, the River Conway follows the faulted junction of the Ordovician rocks of Snowdonia and the Silurian rocks of the Denbighshire Moors. The fault-zone is marked by an impressive wall-like escarpment, rising over 1,000 feet from the valley floor at

FIG. 14 (a).   The lower Conway valley, showing the Dolgarrog escarpment.

FIG. 14 (b).   Key to aerial photograph — 1. Llanrwst.   2. Fault-line escarpment.   3. Dolgarrog aluminium works.   4. River Conway. 5. Great Orme, Llandudno.   6. Slopes rising gently towards Denbigh Moors.   7. Irish Sea.

20 feet. The fall from the 'hanging' tributary to the main valley provides the head of water necessary to drive turbines. Afon Porthllwyd flows from Llyn Eigiau and descends about 700 feet to the Conway valley within a quarter of a mile of Afon Ddu which drains Llyn Cowlyd. At Dolgarrog the hydro-electricity so generated was originally used in the working of aluminium; however, the power is nowadays fed into the National Grid, whence Dolgarrog Aluminium Works derives its supply.

Fig. 14 shows part of the middle section of the lower Conway valley looking northwards towards Conway and the Great Orme. The contrast between the sheer slopes of the fault-line escarpment of the west or left side of the valley and the more gentle gradients of the east side is very evident.

ANTICLINES AND SYNCLINES

Two major orogenies or mountain-building processes, the Caledonian of Silurian-Devonian times, and the Armorican or Hercynian of Carboniferous-Permian times, affected the structure of Wales (Appendix III). These tectonic movements slowly raised the sedimentary rocks from beneath the sea and caused compressional forces to work in a horizontal direction. These forces, in turn, caused the strata to buckle into upfolds and downfolds along well-marked zones of crustal weakness. The axes of the Caledonian folds were aligned north-east to south-west, those of the Armorican were aligned east-west.

Rarely, however, do we find in Wales the comparatively simple relationship of upfold corresponding to hill range and downfold to valley. In the buckling process the crests of the upfolds were stretched and cracked, the bottoms of the downfolds compressed and compacted. When upfolds were raised above the surrounding land, the exposed rocks were attacked by the forces of sub-aerial erosion. Erosion by running water was, and still is, the most important and normal means of land sculpture of the Welsh countryside, though, in past geological times, there were periods when desert conditions prevailed and wind erosion was temporarily paramount. At other times, conditions were glacial and ice erosion was dominant. Thus, by a variety of agents, denudation has persisted, and the height of the land surface progressively reduced.

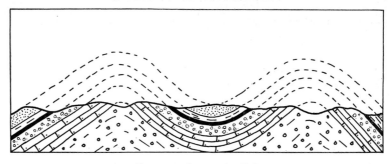

FIG. 15. Inverted relief.

Rocks vary in their resistance to the forces of erosion; 'weak' strata are etched out more quickly than more resistant strata. At one time it was also thought that erosion concentrated more effectively on stretched and weakened upfold crests than on the compressed and compacted trough of downfolds. Some doubt is now attached to this view since all parts of all folds must experience varying degrees of compression. However, once the protecting arch of resistant rock has been removed, erosion rapidly removes any softer rocks in the core of the upfold, leaving the hard bands to stand out as escarpments with sharp in-facing slopes (Fig. 15). Such escarpments may persist for a surprising time, but, like the softer strata, they, too, are eventually reduced to a lower altitude than the compressed sediments at the base of the downfold. In this way, relief may be finally 'inverted', the enduring base of the downfold remaining as a mountain or as high ground, and the axis of the upfold as a valley. By the time the final stages in the cycle of erosion are attained, the land is reduced to a gently undulating surface, known as a peneplain (p. 31). This surface cuts across or truncates rocks of varying structure and resistance to erosion. In this way the mountains thrown up by both the Caledonian and the Armorican orogenies were denuded and worn down to peneplains.

It follows from what has been said that the upfolds and downfolds visible in the present landscape of Wales are mere vestiges of larger folds of Caledonian or Armorican times which have long since been obliterated by incessant erosion.

Probably the closest approximation to a structural downfold coinciding with a depression in Wales is at Caerphilly, Glamorgan (154, 1586). Here, in the south trough or downfold between the Pontypridd-Maesteg anticline and the southern outcrop of the

C

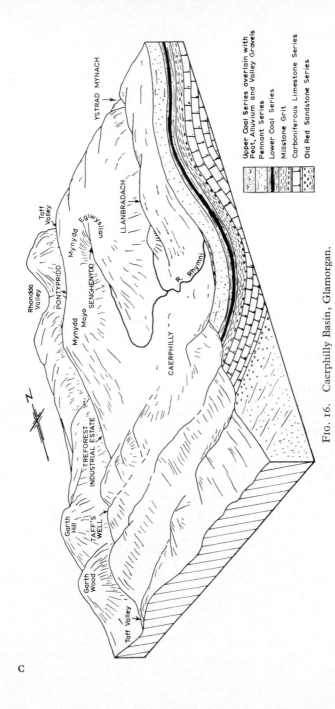

FIG. 16. Caerphilly Basin, Glamorgan.

Upper Coal Series overlain with
Peat, Alluvium and Valley Gravels

Pennant Series

Lower Coal Series

Millstone Grit

Carboniferous Limestone Series

Old Red Sandstone Series

N

Rhondda Valley

PONTYPRIDD

Taff Valley

Mynydd Eglwysilan

Mynydd Mayo SENGHENYDD

CAERPHILLY

YSTRAD MYNACH

LLANBRADACH

R. Rhymni

TREFOREST INDUSTRIAL ESTATE

Garth Hill
TAFF'S WELL

Garth Wood

Taff Valley

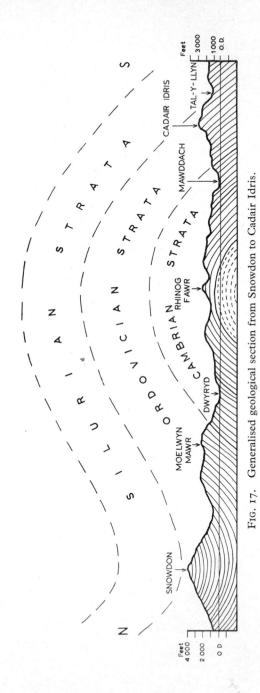

FIG. 17. Generalised geological section from Snowdon to Cadair Idris.

Coalfield lies an elevated basin at a height of 300 feet O.D. floored by Upper Coal Series strata and surrounded by higher ground, 800–1,000 feet O.D., composed of Pennant grits. The lower ground corresponds to the base of the downfold and the higher ground to the limbs of the downfold (Fig. 16). The floor of the basin is covered with extensive deposits of coarse glacial material which have been heaped into irregular ridges and drumlins, interspersed with peat bogs and alluvial flats. Nearby, at Bedwas, where the River Rhymni leaves the basin, a 400-yard-wide gorge has been excavated through a terminal moraine (172883, p. 100).

The summit of Snowdon (3,560 feet), the highest point on the land surface of Wales, is also at the base of a major downfold. The volcanic lavas and ashes, sedimentary rocks and igneous intrusions of Ordovician age that form this imposing pyramidal peak, form an intricate and detailed structure, but, in general, they are disposed as a broad downfold, between upfolds of older rocks, one to the north in the Caernarvon-Llanberis-Bangor district, and one to the south in the Rhinog Mountains (Harlech Dome) (Fig. 17). Fig. 19 shows the summit from the north-east on the ridge between Crib-y-Ddysgl and Crib Goch. The veneer of snow on the wind-swept slope picks out the synclinal structure (Fig. 18) which is clearly discernible just beneath the summit. Disintegration of the bare rock of the sheer cliff-like wall beneath the summit has led to the extensive accumulation of unstable *scree* (p. 62) through which wind the final stages of the '*Pyg* Track' (*P*(en) *y* *G*(wryd)) to the summit.

In complete contrast to the downfold or synclinal structure of Snowdon, the valleys of the Rivers Teifi and Tywi both follow, in part, the crest lines of structural upfolds or anticlines, aptly designated the Teifi and Tywi anticlines, separated by the high ground of the broad Central Wales syncline.

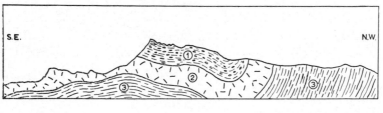

1. Tuffs   2. Lavas   3. Grits and Shales

FIG. 18.   Structure of Snowdon.

FIG. 19. Snowdon viewed from the north-east. Note the downfold near the summit and the extensive scree formations below.

Igneous Features

THE movements with which were associated the folding, fracturing and shattering of the earth's crust also gave rise to zones of surface weakness. At such zones there is a local decrease of pressure which allows deeply buried material (magma) to assume a liquid molten state and seep upwards along the lines of weakness. Sometimes the lava is *extruded* at the surface, at others it does not actually break the overlying rocks but merely *intrudes* into them. In either case, intrusions or extrusions, and particularly after a long period of denudation, the landscape form is very considerably influenced by the presence of igneous (Latin — *ignis*, fire) material.

Solidified lava conduits with central volcanic vents stand out as 'necks' or 'plugs' long after the cones of the original volcano have disappeared. Lavas which welled up along faults or fissures give rise to lava plateaux. Where the lava is injected along the bedding-planes of adjacent rocks, a horizontal sheet or *sill* is formed; that injected into and consolidated in more or less vertical cracks gives a vertical or highly inclined sheet or *dyke*. Sills after tilting and erosion often give rise to escarpments, dykes remain as wall-like structures if they are more resistant than the rocks through which they have cut, or as broad hollows or gullies, if less resistant (Fig. 20).

A volcano (possibly submarine), fully established in North Wales in Cambrian times, gave forth lavas and ashes that are now found on Rhobell Fawr. The greatest period of vulcanicity, however, came

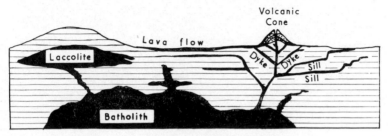

FIG. 20. Main types of igneous intrusion.

later in Ordovician times when the principal rocks of Arennig Fawr, Cadair Idris and Snowdonia, were either poured out on to the sea-bed or else intruded into existing strata. It is the features carved from these volcanic rocks that now hold such strong appeal for the climber and the lover of mountain scenery.

Different from volcanoes such as Vesuvius (Italy), Fuji-yama (Japan), or Paricutin (Andes), whose ashes and lavas were poured out over the land, the Ordovician volcanoes of Wales were often submarine; in this case their lavas poured out on the sea-floor (pillow lavas) are now almost always interbedded with marine sediments. Snowdon provides a vivid illustration of this fact and of the magnitude of the subsequent mountain-building processes, for at the summit are two sets of volcanic rocks separated by a thin bed of sedimentary strata in which are to be found trilobites, brachiopods and other marine fossils.

The form, position and disposition of the several igneous features of Wales that will now be considered can only be fully appreciated in the light of this initial vulcanicity, subsequent mountain-building processes and later denudation. The Ordovician vulcanicity was followed by the Caledonian Orogeny (earth-movements) which threw volcanic and sedimentary strata into great folds and to great heights above sea-level. The mountains so formed were of much the same order of magnitude as our present-day Alps. Their structures too were similar though not as complicated. But subsequent denudation of the arched-up rocks has so reduced the surface, that the relief features seen today are but remnants of former imposing masses, very different from what prevailed when the lavas and igneous intrusions were first formed. Much of what is seen now is the result of the Pleistocene glaciation and, geologically speaking, almost a thing of yesterday.

LAVA FLOWS

The straightforward division of igneous rocks into extrusive and intrusive is not clear-cut when applied to Wales. A large proportion is made up of those best described as 'contemporaneous' and they occur principally in Snowdonia and Cadair Idris, although they are not unknown elsewhere. They are actually extrusions, but resemble

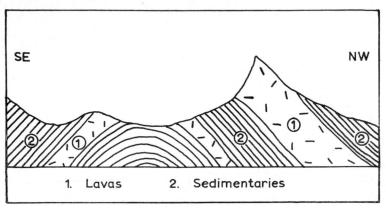

SE   NW

1. Lavas   2. Sedimentaries

FIG. 21.   Structure of Tryfan.

intrusions in that they may not have been finally exposed until
sedimentary covering layers were removed by erosion.

During the Ordovician Period Snowdonia was the trough of a
giant syncline in the Cambrian rocks which lies some 17,000 feet
below the present sea-level.   In this Ordovician sea were deposited
thick layers of sedimentary rocks which are today's shales and
mudstones.   Periodically, however, the Ordovician age witnessed a
series of volcanic outpourings or extrusions on to the sea-bed which,
having spread and solidified, soon became covered by the sedimentary
deposition which was then resumed on top of them, although it is
probable that several of the volcanic cones were able to rise above
sea-level.   In consequence, volcanic rocks such as these *rhyolites* are
interbedded with the sedimentary rocks which were being laid down
during the same period.   Such volcanic rocks appear in at least five
different positions in the Ordovician succession.   What is more,
when these horizontal beds were folded — and often overfolded —
in the Caledonian Period of earth-movements which succeeded the
Ordovician vulcanicity, the igneous beds were folded with the
sedimentary in exactly the same way and have been exposed in
numerous locations by subsequent erosion.

Tryfan (107, 663592) provides a good example of such a lava flow
(Figs. 21 and 22).   The peak itself is composed of lavas of the second
group of extrusions in the Ordovician sequence which are found
between two beds of shales.   The peak forms one arm of a denuded
anticline, the base of which is now Bwlch Tryfan; the eastern limb
is provided by Gallt-yr-Ogof and the whole complex is a fine

example of inverted relief. Frost weathering in the well-jointed lavas has produced both the massive craggy face which overlooks Llyn Ogwen and the famous 'two figures' at the summit — two vertical rocks often mistaken for men when they are clearly picked out from the main road, A5, which runs below. The lavas dip away from the viewpoint at an angle of 60° underneath the Cwm Idwal syncline behind Tryfan.

The summit of Carnedd Ddafydd (663630) is etched in strata of similar origin, a gentle anticline at Ffynnon Lloer bringing the rock up again on the southern slopes. Glyder Fawr has a summit composed of steeply-dipping lavas of the next major extrusion after those of Carnedd Ddafydd and Tryfan (Lower Snowdon lavas) while the col (6358) above Devil's Kitchen between Glyder Fawr and Y Garn lies in volcanic tuffs produced by explosions during the same period of vulcanicity. Snowdon itself is also capped by these tuffs forming the base of a syncline whose limbs have long since been removed (p. 17). The material here is not wholly volcanic; some of it was re-sorted in the deep water of the Ordovician sea, and is often inter-stratified with marine sediments of the same period.

FIG. 22.   Tryfan from the east. The lavas themselves dip *away* from the observer at an angle of 60°.

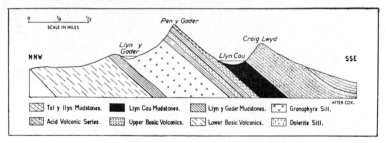

FIG. 23. Geological section through Cadair Idris escarpment.

SILLS

Magma which fails to break through overlying rock and reach the surface is often intruded into zones of weakness along more or less horizontal bedding-planes to produce a tabular sheet of rock known as a *sill*. When such a sill and its associated strata are tilted, the resistant edge of the sill is commonly exposed by denudation to form a prominent escarpment.

A striking Welsh landscape feature formed in this way is the dominating north-facing escarpment of Cadair Idris, overlooking the scenically beautiful area around Dolgellau and the Barmouth estuary. Structurally the escarpment is part of the southern flank of the Harlech Dome anticline, but it is formed mainly of a thick granophyre sill emplaced among Ordovician lavas, pyroclastic deposits, sediments and dolerite intrusive rocks. The main intrusion of granophyre (acid igneous rock) is, in fact, composed of two parts, one which is sill-like and the other which transgresses not only associated rocks but also overlying sills of dolerite — a dark-coloured fine-textured basic igneous rock (Fig. 23).

Fig. 24 is the view of the Cadair Idris escarpment looking south. The main scarp due to the granophyre sill forms Mynydd Moel, Foxes Path and Cyfrwy. The granophyre is followed above by mudstones and extercalated ash bands, dolerite, ashes and pillow lavas. Extensive accumulations of *scree* (p. 62) can be clearly seen at the foot of the cliffs on the right of the picture.

Several of the Snowdonian mountains have some of their characteristic features due to outcropping sills of igneous rock. Y Cnicht, for example, between Beddgelert and Blaenau Ffestiniog

FIG. 24 (a).   Cadair Idris from the north.   The cirque lake, Llyn y Gadair, lies out of sight in the centre of the escarpment. Note the extensive scree accumulations footing the escarpment.

has its steeply inclined sediments and volcanic ashes of Ordovician age, strongly reinforced by a dolerite sill which has been injected between the stratified rocks.   Viewed from the south-east Cnicht looks like a mile-long ridge, but from the south-west it presents a sharp peak not unlike the Swiss Matterhorn.

The same dolerite forms the summit of Carnedd Llywelyn and the precipices (Ysgolion Duon) on the northern face of Carnedd Ddafydd.   Moel Siabod, too, has its summit and spurs carved out of a large sill-like mass of dolerite.

In Pembrokeshire, in the vicinity of St. David's, Carn Llidi (151, 7328), Carn Lleithr (7428), etc., which rise as monadnocks above the coastal platforms (Fig. 106, p. 129), are composed of sills of intrusive dolerite.   They have attained a more or less vertical position

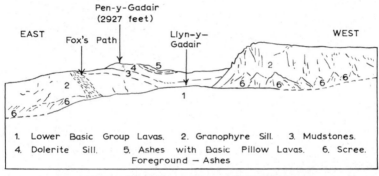

1. Lower Basic Group Lavas.   2. Granophyre Sill.   3. Mudstones.
4. Dolerite Sill.   5. Ashes with Basic Pillow Lavas.   6. Scree.
Foreground — Ashes

FIG. 24 (b).   Key to view of Cadair Idris.

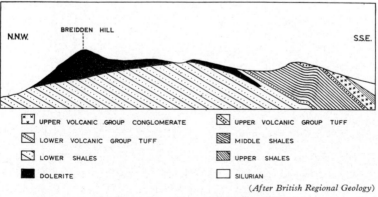

(*After British Regional Geology*)

FIG. 25.   Structure of Breidden Hill.

FIG. 26. The Breidden Hill and Moel-y-Golfa, Montgomeryshire.

through having been folded at the same time as the sedimentary rocks into which they were injected. In this same area the headlands of St. David's Head, Strumble Head and Pen Pleidian are all essentially sills of dolerite. In fact, every headland between Ramsey Island and Strumble is of igneous rocks and every inlet and bay carved out of sedimentary strata (p. 125).

The rounded regularity of outline that characterises the landforms of Central Wales is broken in the Wells area by the presence of bare crags of igneous rocks and a more varied scenery. Here there are several igneous sills at Builth and at Gelli Hill (128, 0958) south-east of Llandrindod. The Breidden Hills, six miles north-east of Welshpool, and near the Welsh Border, have an andesite sill and also dolerite intruded into strata which have adopted an anticlinal form (Figs. 25 and 26).

DYKES

As already noted, earth-movements and igneous activity during mainly Pre-Cambrian and Ordovician times gave rise to the intrusion of magma into overlying rocks. Where the magma rose through vertical fissures, or cut *across* the bedding-planes, a solidified wall

of rock or *dyke* remains.   Long-continued denudation has exposed
these dykes which, if composed of resistant rock, stand out as ridges;
at other time they form narrow depressions.   Such dykes are

FIG. 27.   A basalt dyke in Carboniferous Limestone,
Traeth Bychan, Anglesey.

numerous in Anglesey, Llŷn, Bardsey Island, Pembrokeshire and Snowdonia.

Those of Anglesey and Llŷn pass uninterruptedly across the bedding-planes, folds and other structures of the Pre-Cambrian complexes and later rocks, but owing to the heavy cover of glacial drift they are rarely seen away from the coast. In some instances in Llŷn the dykes may be 50–60 feet wide, but the more usual dimensions are between 4 and 20 feet. Fig. 27 shows a dyke of dark basaltic rock cutting through horizontally disposed Carboniferous Limestone strata in the cliff at Traeth Bychan, Anglesey (106, 517846).

VOLCANIC PLUGS

The vulcanicity which was active in Caernarvonshire 350–375 million years ago was due, in no small measure, to the presence of what is now called the Padarn Ridge which extends some 13 miles south-west to north-east from near Llanllyfni to the neighbourhood of Bethesda. This ridge of ancient crystalline rocks, which at that time was overlain by great thicknesses of Cambrian and Ordovician strata, proved an immovable obstacle to lateral pressures from the south-east. In consequence, strata forced against it were piled up against the ridge on its south-east side. North-east to south-west lines of weakness were set up through which fluid lavas subsequently flowed and from which ashes were ejected. The centres of volcanic eruption were all situated along a line south-east of the Padarn Ridge and its prolongation. The wide extent of some of the Caernarvonshire lava-flows and their general characters seem to be consistent with a submarine origin, though it is not impossible that some of the vents were above sea-level, certainly for part of the time.

By studying the form and character of the various igneous rocks in Caernarvonshire, Harker (1889) was able to reconstruct the location of these ancient volcanoes and their probable sphere of activity (Fig. 28). Composed of fine-grained, crystalline rocks which rise steeply through their enclosing strata, Penmaen Mawr, Foel Frâs (3,000 feet), Mynydd Perfedd (2,665 feet), Mynydd Mawr (2,291 feet) (Fig. 29), Clynnog-fawr, Cefn Fadryn and Yr Eifl (1,849 feet) were thought by him to represent the 'plugs' of igneous rock which solidified within the orifices of the ancient volcanoes.

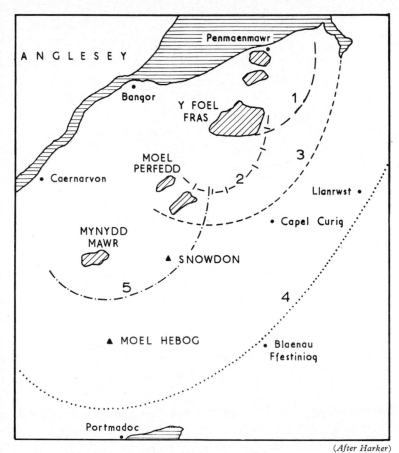

FIG. 28.   Ancient volcanoes of Snowdonia.

1. Acid intrusive rocks
2. Sedimentary slates and shales

FIG. 29.   Structure of Mynydd Mawr, Caernarvonshire.

Subsequent accumulation has, of course, obliterated any direct or obvious connection there might have been between the 'plugs' and the lavas, interbedded with sedimentary rocks, but the roughly circular ground plan of these igneous masses and the way in which adjacent strata have been altered by heat offers reasonable justification for assuming them to be the 'throats' or 'necks' of ancient volcanoes.

In Llŷn, where a platform about 270 feet above sea-level is the basic element in the relief, igneous intrusions stand out as islands from the peninsula. The most famous of these are the triple peaks of Yr Eifl (often corrupted in English to 'The Rivals') rising to 1,849 feet above sea-level, which are thought to represent the cores of ancient volcanoes that flourished in Ordovician times. Carn Fadrun (Fig. 30) is another example in the same area.

FIG. 30. Carn Fadrun, Caernarvonshire. Note the way in which these peaks stand out above the surrounding low platform-like surface.

Gradational Features

FLUVIAL FEATURES
(The Work of Streams)

In the introduction, Wales was divided into landscape regions, the most basic differences noted being between highland and lowland. The principal lowlands were either large river valleys, or low plateaux reduced to such by erosional forces, in this case either rivers or the sea. In the case of the highlands, the distinction was drawn between severely glaciated mountains, such as those of Snowdonia and the Rhinogs, and the hills and mountains where, although the effects of glaciation are often present, they are never as dominant as they are in the former areas. But even in the regions of most severe mountain glaciation, the glacial landforms can only be interpreted as modifications or alterations of a previous landscape which had been built up by a protracted period of river erosion. It would, therefore, appear fair to conclude that river erosion is the most important single agent of degradation which has worked to produce the present Welsh landscape, even though many of the most striking individual features are products of severe glaciation, or, in some cases, coastal erosion.

Students will be familiar with the sequence of development of a river valley from the young stage through the mature to the old-age stage. The general landscape goes through the same stages (Fig. 31), and the 'old-age' product of erosion, characterised by a land surface of faint relief, is called a *peneplain*. This final stage is reached when all the rivers have gone on eroding into what might previously have been an upland for such a long period of time that their gradients have been reduced to the degree when no more erosion is possible. The streams now only have enough energy to take their waters to the sea, and are unable either to carry a load or even to acquire one. This, however, is only a theoretical stage, and is never actually reached in practice ; indeed, it is difficult to point to a true example of old age in rivers in Wales today.

This absence of old-age rivers is due to one important qualification which must be made when discussing this 'Cycle of Stream

D

Young

Mature

Old

FIG. 31. Diagrammatic impression of theoretical stages in landscape evolution under conditions of normal stream erosion.

Erosion' (as the 'young–mature–old' sequence is termed). This is that the hypothesis of the cycle assumes that the processes concerned are uninterrupted by changes in the level of the land surface with respect to sea-level. A lowering of sea-level or an uplift of the land *rejuvenates* the rivers, *i.e.* makes them young again. Now the rivers have energy to cut down into the former peneplain, forming gorges at first, which gradually widen into mature valleys, and this process, if it goes on long enough, will reduce the land to another peneplain, at a lower level. Thus the cycle is repeated.

The important point is, however, that after uplift has taken place and the newly-invigorated river has eroded into the former peneplain, fragments of the old peneplain may well be left, even when the rejuvenated river has formed a new peneplain beneath the old one. The picture now is of a flat or gently rolling peneplain meandered across by old-age rivers, but standing up out of it will be remnants of the former peneplain into which this one has been cut after the rejuvenation of the river.

Obviously, this process can be repeated an indefinite number of times. In most districts of Upland Wales, the predominant impression gained in viewing the scene from a hilltop is uniformity and flatness, broken occasionally by a deeply cut valley. E. H. Brown (1957(a) and 1960), basing his work upon careful field observation of remnant surfaces, has postulated that there are, in fact, three principal levels at which uplifted peneplains are found in Wales, and that fragments of all three levels can be correlated throughout the country. Between 1,700 and 2,000 feet is found the 'High

Plateau', between 1,200 and 1,600 feet the 'Middle Peneplain' and between 800 and 1,000 feet the 'Low Peneplain'. In addition, the top plateau surface is surmounted by a 'Monadnock Group' which includes Snowdonia, the Berwyn and Aran Mountains, Plynlimon, the Black Mountains and Brecon Beacons. Finally, around the coast, and extending up to 20 miles inland, Brown and others have recognised a series of marine-eroded platforms, the highest having an upper limit at 650–700 feet above sea-level (p. 118).

Brown's view of three successive sub-aerial peneplains uplifted one above the other and topped by the monadnock group is a contribution of outstanding importance to the understanding of Welsh landforms, yet it would be wrong to assume that it has been accepted unreservedly, as it stands, as the final answer. Critics have pointed out that the altitudinal correlation of remnant hilltops is dangerous, as there is no reason to suppose that the hilltops have not been worn down to some degree also. Brown, however, forestalled this criticism at least partially by using a technique of finding one particular erosion surface and following it as far as it went, thus reducing to a minimum his dependence upon the correlation of hilltops. Again, the designation of the Middle and Lower Peneplains as 'worthy examples of the Davisian peneplain' has been questioned. It is suggested that the original pre-uplift landscape in the case of the lower two surfaces had not, in fact, reached the peneplain level, but was a maturely dissected upland. Moreover, the possibility that there may have been an element of marine planation in the lowest of Brown's 'sub-aerial' surfaces has been suggested. Challinor (1930) maintains that in Cardiganshire it is unnecessary to accept the fundamental idea of uplifted peneplains at all in order to explain the landforms.

Nevertheless, if it is accepted that these plateau levels are the basic elements in the Welsh landscape, then it is necessary to accept that river erosion, which produced at least two, and probably three of them, is the most fundamental agent which has played a part in the processing of the landforms of the country. It follows that glaciation has done no more than produce a number of striking modifications upon a river-moulded landscape, and this is by far the most fruitful approach to the study of the glacial landforms of Wales.

With the above considerations in mind, it is possible to consider some of the more important river-moulded landforms which are common in, and characteristic of, Wales.

FIG. 32. Youthful valley with interlocking spurs: upper reaches of River Clydach near Llangadog, Carmarthenshire.

YOUTHFUL VALLEYS

The rain and snow which fall on the mountains and moorlands of Wales — the equivalent of anything from 60 to 200 inches of rainfall per year — flows under gravity, collects into small streamlets, and these, in turn, combine to form main streams. In their upper reaches or 'torrent tracts' the streams occupy mere notches in the land surface, the amount of water being less than downstream. Characteristic of this stage is the headward erosion and rapid down-cutting (vertical corrasion) of the narrow, steeply and irregularly graded river-bed, a process which proceeds at a faster rate than the wearing away of the valley sides by rain and running water.

Vertical corrasion is achieved through the abrasive power of the pebbles rolled along or carried in suspension (the 'load'), while irregularities in the stream-bed arise through variations in the litho-logical character of the strata over which the water flows. The result is a steep-sided valley with a V-shaped cross-section and interlocking or interdigitating spurs.

Fig. 32 is the view looking up the valley of the River Clydach, a left-bank tributary of the River Tywi at a point (140, 738197) where it is crossed by the road from Llangadog over the Black Mountain to Brynaman. This 'young' or 'youthful' valley shows the steep-sided rock-strewn V-shaped valley with interlocking spurs. Figs. 32 and 33 are so typical of most upland areas that further specific examples are unnecessary.

Where the swift-flowing water encounters an obstruction, eddies may well form small whirlpools causing stones to rotate in hollows.

FIG. 33.   Youthful valley: Ebwy north of Crumlin, Monmouthshire.

FIG. 34.   Pot-holes in the River Taff at Pontypridd, Glamorgan.

These rotating stones become rounded pebbles and, acting with a sort of mortar and pestle action, help form cylindrical hollows known as pot-holes. One series of pot-holes is clearly visible (Fig. 34) in the bed of the River Taff at Pontypridd (154, 072898). The Blue Pool (Pwll Glas) on the Taff Fechan at Pontsarn (154, 045098) near Merthyr Tydfil is a better-known example, while the Devil's Cauldron at the famous beauty spot at Devil's Bridge (127, 7477) is but a series of enlarged and connected pot-holes through which rush the waters of the turbulent Mynach.

Only infrequently does a stream flow over rocks of uniform hardness. Usually hard beds alternate with soft beds. The youthful stream in its down-cutting action is more successful with the soft rocks than with the hard ones, and so irregularities of gradient occur in the stream-bed. Such irregularities commonly give rise to rapids or waterfalls. The attractive waterfall, Sgŵd-yr-Eira (Fig. 35) on the River Hepste (141, 9310), one of the headwaters of the River Neath, was formed in this way. A fault first caused the stream to flow from a hard, well-jointed sandstone on to relatively soft shales. The scouring action of the water at the base of the fall undercut into the softer rocks beneath to form a 'plunge-pool', whilst the incessant undermining caused pieces of the hard cap-rock to break off when left without support. Consequently the fall is gradually receding upstream. In this respect and in its essential characteristics, Sgŵd-yr-Eira compares with Niagara Falls. The deep pool visible at the base of the fall, and the amphitheatre-like expansion of the youthful valley at this point are typically associated with waterfalls. Apart from wading the river, the recess in the rocks beneath the fall provides the only convenient crossing of the river at this point. (Note the Scout troop in Fig. 35).

While irregularities in the stream-bed are a common cause of waterfalls, they may also be the result of river capture, *i.e.* the differences in level between capture and captured stream (see p. 52), as in the case of the Swallow Falls at Betws-y-Coed (107, 7756) and the Mynach Falls at Devil's Bridge (127, 7477), or of glacial over-deepening of main valleys (see p. 80) in relation to side valleys, causing waters to plunge suddenly into the main valley from the higher level (hanging valley). This last type of waterfall is foremost in Snowdonia.

FIG. 35. Sgŵd-yr-Eira waterfall on the River Hepste
near Pontneddfechan, Glamorgan.

MATURE VALLEYS

Downstream where the gradient of the river-bed is reduced and
the speed of flow of the river is checked, down-cutting becomes
relatively slow. The main work of the river is now transportation,
of sand, silt and mud in suspension, and the rolling of pebbles along
the bed. *Lateral* corrasion now assumes the ascendancy. Chance
obstacles or irregularities due to structural variations cause the river
to swing, the current eroding the outer or concave bank and depositing material on the inside or convex bank where the current is
slack. Interlocking spurs, features so common to the youthful stage,
are cut off or truncated and the valley becomes increasingly open in
cross profile. When this, the mature valley tract, is reached, the
valley possesses a wide, flat floor bounded by a simple line of steep

cliffs or 'bluffs'. At this stage, the meanders of the river normally swing through the width of the flood plain of the river.

The swinging meanders and wide alluvial plain of the River Tywi are well illustrated in Fig. 36 (152, 4120). Between Llandovery and Carmarthen the Tywi follows a long stretch with only a very slight decrease of height, and during times of heavy rain the flood waters frequently overtop the river-bank and spread outwards over the alluvial plain. This air view shows the town of Carmarthen sited on a terrace (p. 49) on the north side or right bank of the river, and a landscape of cultivated fields in a patchwork of irregularly shaped enclosures and clumps of woodland.

In Cardiganshire, the River Rheidol has incised itself into the coastal plateau (Fig. 37). This view (looking westwards from 127, 685782) shows the river flowing towards its outlet into the sea at Aberystwyth. The valley floor is wide and flat and occupied by cultivated land, skirted by steep valley sides, picturesquely wooded with a cultivated plateau surface above. In this lower part of the river's course, vertical erosion has become subordinated to lateral

FIG. 36. Meanders in the River Tywi at Carmarthen.

FIG. 37.   Meanders in the River Rheidol east of Aberystwyth,
Cardiganshire.

erosion, and the river swings from side to side in graceful meanders.
The loops will probably not grow much beyond this size, but they
will gradually shift downstream.   In this way, the alluvium of the
flood plain is constantly worked over by the river.

It is true that some meanders are caused by obstacles or irregularities in the river valley, and yet it must be admitted that some of
the best formed and regular meanders are found in virtually homo-
geneous material (alluvial deposits) free of obstacles.   In short, the
development of meanders is still not fully understood.   Since
examples are so obvious and numerous all over Wales, it is pointless
to quote further examples.

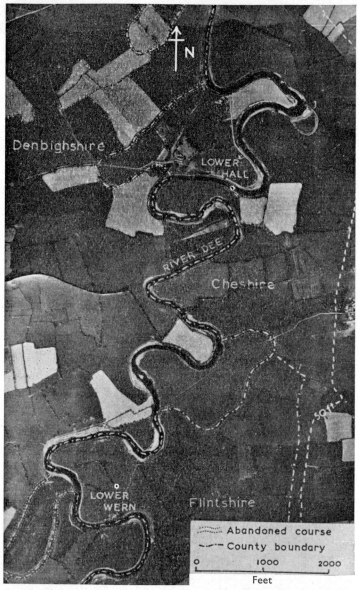

FIG. 38. Meanders of the River Dee between Bangor-on-Dee and Holt. This vertical air view shows how the county boundaries still follow former courses although these have long since been abandoned by the river.

OLD-AGE VALLEYS

The old-age stage is characterised by a sluggish flow over a very wide and gently-graded flood plain. Deposition is extensive; erosion is absent. The lazy river wanders freely, unfettered by structural influences associated with the bed rock since the valley is now generally occupied by great thicknesses of alluvium.

It seems unlikely that any one river in Wales is in the extreme stage of old age, though the lower reaches of the River Dee in Flintshire and Denbighshire certainly exhibit some characteristic features of this stage. The vertical air view of the River Dee near Holt (Fig. 38) shows the intricate meanders of the river as it wanders over the Cheshire Plain. The river has gradually shifted its course over the years, and abandoned meanders are clearly visible. The county boundaries bear witness to this phenomenon, for at one time they followed the meanders of the river, but in several places no longer do so. Meanders continue to become more and more complicated, and the curves become more acute, till in time of flood the river breaks through the narrow neck of land between two near-by loops in order to follow a more direct route. The ends are blocked

FIG. 39. Ox-bow lake at Llandderfel, near Corwen, Merioneth.

by alluvium, and the loop is isolated and abandoned. The small curved lake that remains is called a 'cut-off', 'ox-bow' or 'mortlake'.

Fig. 39 is an example of an ox-bow on the River Dee at Llandderfel (117, 992367). It is only a matter of time before vegetation growing in the stagnant water converts the lake into a marsh. This has happened to a section of the River Ely near the cricket pitch at Miskin Manor (154, 055804). Later, with the aid of flood detritus, the loop is eventually entirely filled to form, once again, part of the flood plain. A good example of this later stage is found on the River Clwyd at Rhuddlan (108, 0277), and again on the River Ely in Glamorgan near the playing-fields at Pontyclun (154, 035808).

In time, a river succeeds in carving out a course that falls in a curve (*thalweg*) from the steeper part near its source to the almost flat section near its mouth. This is the generalised pattern, but obviously some rivers do not conform to this scheme. In Wales many rivers tumble direct from the uplands to the sea and demonstrate only youthful characteristics along the whole length of their course. Others are relatively mature and are associated with a later stage in the cycle of erosion. As noted, the old-age stage is rarely attained, and apart, possibly, from the lower reaches of the River Dee in north-east Wales and the lower reaches of the Ely and Rhymni in South Wales, this must remain a theoretical stage as far as the rivers of Wales are concerned.

ALLUVIAL FANS

Since the weight of the largest particle any stream can carry varies approximately as the sixth power of its velocity, it follows that any sudden decrease in velocity will result in deposition. In Wales, where deep valleys are numerous, and where 'hanging' tributaries frequently cascade hundreds of feet down on to flat valley floors beneath, such deposition is common. It takes the form of a fan-shaped delta of alluvium over which the depositing stream flows. As the stream clogs its own course, so it is forced to find a new one, and the aggradation is resumed elsewhere in the fan. It is clear, however, that the coarsest pebbles and boulders will be put down first at the head of the fan; from here the material will become gradually finer, grading eventually to the finest material of all where the tributary joins the main river.

F IG. 40.   Lake delta at Llangower Point on the south side of Llyn Tegid.

Amongst the larger examples in Wales are those at Abergynolwyn (127, 6706) and Dol-y-Cae (116, 7211) in the Tal-y-llyn valley of Merionethshire.   In South Wales, a fine example occurs near Gilwern in south-east Breconshire, where the wide extension of the 200-foot contour (141, 2415 and 2515) indicates an alluvial fan spread out by the River Clydach.   Rarely, however, are these fans so easily detectable on either 1-inch or 1 : 25000 sheets; most readers will know of their own local examples.

Where a rapidly flowing tributary disgorges into a lake, a more conspicuous feature may result.   In this case, the level of the water outlines the shape of the fan and emphasises what would otherwise be a comparatively insignificant landform.   We have already noted the delta on the bank of Tal-y-llyn Lake (Fig. 6) at Pentre Dolamarch (116, 7110), and two more fine instances can be cited on the shores of Llyn Tegid (Bala Lake).   These are Llangower Point (117, 9932) on the south-eastern shore (Fig. 40) and at Hen Glanllyn (8932) on the north-western shore.   These, the deltas of the Gower and Llafar respectively, will eventually split and then shorten the lake.   Llyn Ogwen (107, 6560) is rapidly being split by Afon Bochlwyd, and pronounced deltas may be detected around Llyn Gwynant (6551).   At Llanberis (5860 and 5859) the detritus supplied by Afon Arddu has already split the former ribbon lake (p. 82) into two at a point where it was evidently over 100 feet deep (Fig. 41).

Already one or two ribbon lakes have disappeared and others severely shortened in length (p. 83). There is no doubt that, surrounded as they are by steep slopes, and fed by turbulent streams, all Wales' ribbon lakes will eventually fill in this manner.

POLYCYCLIC RELIEF

If a stream which has already reached a late stage of development is given new erosive vigour by means of an uplift of the land or a negative movement of sea-level, down-cutting will be resumed and a young valley excavated in the floor of the former mature valley. Relief of this sort is known as *polycyclic*, since it is the product of more than one cycle of erosion.

It has already been pointed out that the geological history of Wales has consisted of two main periods of mountain building followed by protracted periods of erosion, during which the folded

FIG. 41. Llyn Padarn and Llyn Peris in Snowdonia viewed from the north-west. The detritus brought in by Afon Arddu (*right background*) has split the former ribbon lake in two. The Dinorwic Slate Quarries (*left*) have contributed to the shape of Llyn Peris (*distance*).

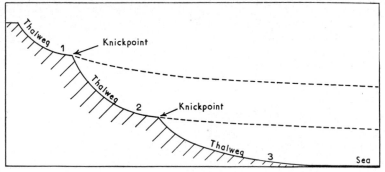

FIG. 42. Long profile (*thalweg*) of a stream showing knickpoints.

hill ranges were reduced to peneplain level (p. 32). The weight of
modern opinion suggests that subsequently a succession of base-level
adjustments transformed the surface into a series of plateaux at
varying levels. The former mature, graded streams which flowed
across the original peneplains were rejuvenated and incised into the
surface. Wales can thus be said to be a land of polycyclic relief.

The long profiles (*thalwegs*) of most Welsh rivers show a number
of *knickpoints*, which often correspond to the breaks of slope between
the various plateau levels of the interior (Fig. 42). No longer, of
course, does the knickpoint coincide with the edge of the plateau
level; by now it will have receded into the uplifted platform as the
rejuvenated stream cuts its gorge. The upper curves will be graded
to a sea-level of former times, and will be fragments of former longer
profiles which are shown on the diagram by dotted lines. If sufficient
of the original profile remains, it is possible to project it seawards
and obtain an approximation for the extent of the uplift which has
occurred.

Brown (1952) attempted to accomplish this study mathematically,
by accurately determining the long profile of the River Ystwyth by
levelling, and then obtaining the best possible 'fit' of a mathematical
curve of a certain form. Here he followed the method of Green
(1936), who had previously worked along similar lines in south-east
England, in interpreting variations of stream base level in connection
with the formation of river terraces. The application of this
interesting method of determining uplifts must, however, be limited;
the vital part of the curve is the graded section (*i.e.* the lower portion),
and it is precisely this part which is all too often already lost. The
lengths of truly graded sections remaining in the Welsh Heartland

are usually small, and are rarely sufficient to warrant a detailed mathematical examination.

The ideal cross-section of a polycyclic valley should show the open topography of the former mature valley dissected by a youthful 'V'. Valley benches can thus often be correlated on either side of the gorge; indeed several pairs of benches at different levels representing the various rejuvenations may often be detected. They can provide valuable evidence of the height of the former profile above present sea-level.

Polycyclic relief abounds in Wales, but there can surely be no better example in such a confined area than that of Ffestiniog district in North Merionethshire (107 or 116, 7041). Here the rivers Cynfal and Teigl flow off a plateau level at about 1,200–1,400 feet (Migneint, p. 91) down on to another platform at 650–700 feet (on which the village of Ffestiniog is situated), finally descending into the mature Dwyryd which meanders along the floor of the Vale of Maentwrog. Into the top platform, the Cynfal has cut a magnificent gorge which ends in a spectacular waterfall (Rhaeadr-y-Cwm 736415) half a mile west of Pont-ar-Afon-Gam (Fig. 43). This youthful gorge (Cwm Cynfal) is just approaching maturity on the 650-foot platform at

Fig. 43.   Rhaeadr-y-Cwm on the Afon Cynfal, 3 miles east of Ffestiniog, Merioneth.   (*Artist's impression.*)

FIG. 44. The lower Cynfal gorge near Ffestiniog, Merioneth, showing youthful ravine incised into the surrounding platform surface.

FIG. 45. Rejuvenation in the Rheidol valley at Devil's Bridge, Cardiganshire. The deep gorge is cut into the former open valley leaving the benches clearly visible on either side.

Bont Newydd (714408) when it gives way to a second ravine (Fig. 44) cut into the surrounding platform, eventually emerging into the Dwyryd at about 30 feet O.D. The Cynfal thus presents a superb

E

example of polycyclic relief, with three distinct base levels and two conspicuous knickpoints, at Rhaeadr-y-Cwm and Bont Newydd. The Teigl, with knickpoints in the upper Cwm and at Pont-y-Pandy (707429), has the same features, and so has the Prysor. Rising on the Migneint moorland region in Llyn Conglog Fawr (116, 7538), the Prysor achieves maturity on the 700-foot platform before reaching Trawsfynydd, when the valley opens out into broad maturity. The next knickpoint and the upper part of the ensuing ravine have been drowned by the reservoir constructed in 1926 to serve the hydro-electricity generating station at Maentwrog, but the polycyclic nature of the Prysor is, nevertheless, clear.

A conspicuous polycyclic cross-section is provided by the River Rheidol in its section just above Devil's Bridge (127, 7477). The gorge between Rheidol Falls and Parson's Bridge has been cut into the floor of a former mature valley, which can be detected plainly on either side of the road A4120 between Devil's Bridge and Ysbyty Cynfyn (755, 790). Fig. 45 shows clearly the V-shaped youthful ravine excavated in the broad floor of the former mature valley. In this case, the rejuvenation has resulted from river capture, the descent from one level to another (p. 59) having provided the river with new erosive vigour.

Fig. 46. High level meanders (1,050–1,100 feet O.D.) of the River Elan upstream of Craig-yr-Alltgoch Reservoir. The broad, open character of the valley is typical of the plateau-like nature of much of the interior of central Wales even though downstream a rejuvenation brings a return to youthful features.

Most Welsh rivers, in fact, are polycyclic, including the Elan, whose broad meanders (128, 8972) above Pont ar Elan (Fig. 46) give little indication of the rejuvenation which is to follow as it flows down via the several reservoirs of the Birmingham Corporation Waterworks through the bleak hills west of Rhayader. In Carmarthenshire, the Tywi and the Cothi rivers, having achieved maturity, show further knickpoints and a return to youthful conditions. The Cothi and its tributaries in particular present a fine example of maturity in the Pumpsaint/Llansawel area (140, 620362), but at Abergorlech (5833) the river has returned once more to a youthful state. Similarly, the Dee in north-east Wales, meandering across a broad flood plain through Bala and Corwen, is rejuvenated at Glyndyfrdwy (117 or 108, 150430), enters a deep gorge, and after incising itself into its former meanders (p. 40-41) eventually opens out again near Holt (Fig. 38) to give the nearest approach in Wales to the old-age stage of river development.

RIVER TERRACES

When a river which has established a flood plain is slightly rejuvenated, it cuts down through its own deposits into the underlying rocks. The original flood plain is then left as a flat area or terrace above the new river level. At a very much later stage the river develops a new flood plain within the first, of which, owing to lateral erosion, only remnants may survive. A series of these terraces may be built up, each terrace marking a change of level, a phase of rejuvenation followed by valley deepening, valley widening and deposition. Terraces lie on the bed-rock, and are graded from the coarser deposits nearer the river to the finer deposits away from the river.

Fig. 47 shows a terrace along the right bank of the River Dyfi between Aberangell and Mallwyd (116, 8410). The river has been slightly rejuvenated, and has cut below the level of the terrace, leaving its former alluvium dry and now occupied by permanent grass.

Similar terraces can be observed flanking the flood plains of most mature Welsh rivers. They are prominent in the Dee Valley north-east of Bala, the lower Conway, the Middle Severn downstream of Llanidloes, the lower Tywi around Carmarthen

FIG. 47.   River terrace in the Dyfi valley,
near Mallwyd, Montgomeryshire.

FIG. 48.   The Tydenham bend on the River Wye near Chepstow.
Note the accumulation of gravel on the inside of the meander (*foreground*).

and the Ely downstream of Llantrisant, as well as in many other
locations.

INCISED MEANDERS

In certain instances rejuvenation has checked further meander
development and set up renewed vertical erosion. Between Ross and

Chepstow meanders in the lower course of the River Wye have been cut into and the river has developed a deep, canyon-like valley while still preserving the loops of its earlier course (Fig. 48). Such *entrenched* meanders are the result of a relatively rapid uplift of the land and corresponding vertical erosion. Where the uplift was more gradual, there was time for a certain amount of lateral shift, and the resulting *ingrown* meanders have a slightly more open character (Fig. 49). Such meanders are to be found on the River Wye upstream of Ross, and again on the River Dee between Llangollen and Glyndyfrdwy (117 or 108).

Just as flood-plain meanders are short-circuited (p. 41), so are incised meanders short-circuited through spurs. In such cases, however, the results are more marked and permanent. A clear example is the abandoned incised meander loop of the Dee near Llangollen, though the process here was assisted by glacial interference (p. 45). Two such meanders of the earlier Dee, one near Llantysilio and the other south of Llangollen, have been abandoned owing to the diversion of the river across their necks (Fig. 50).

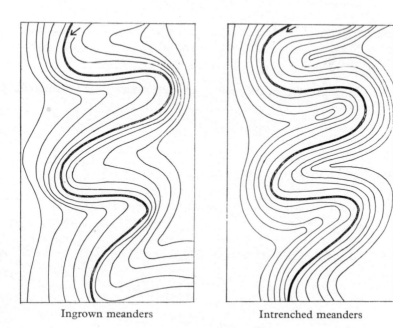

Ingrown meanders   Intrenched meanders

FIG. 49. Incised meanders.

FIG. 50. Incised meanders of the River Dee near Llangollen.

RIVER CAPTURE

The line which separates the drainage basin of a river from an adjacent one is called a water-divide or water-shed. Since both rivers are constantly at work eroding laterally, vertically and headward, this divide may migrate towards one or the other, depending upon the relative erosive power of the two streams. The rate of vertical erosion bears considerably upon that of headward erosion, for the faster a stream is able to cut downwards, the faster the rate at which it can excavate its valley headward into previously uneroded land.

In Fig. 51 suppose stream A is rapidly eroding vertically and headward, whereas stream B, for reasons outlined below, is in a more mature stage, possessing substantially less erosive power and graded to a higher base level. It is clear that, whatever the relative sizes of the two streams, headward erosion by stream A will eventually reach stream B. If, when this occurs, A is at a lower level than B, river capture will occur. B will now turn through 90° and its waters will use the valley of the 'pirate' stream A for a more direct exit to the sea. The former valley of B below the point of capture will contain a small *misfit* stream, of a size inconsistent with that of its valley. B is said to have been *beheaded*; frequently its former valley may contain no stream of any consequence and is called a *wind-gap*.

These circumstances may seem exceptional, but in fact are not so. On the contrary, two adjacent non-parallel streams will only in the most exceptional circumstances have similar base levels and rates of erosion, and some form of capture is almost certain to occur sooner or later. The wide difference in erosive power between one stream and another is, in Wales, usually accounted for by one of two circumstances:

(*a*) The pirate stream may have a shorter distance to travel to reach the sea than the captured; its gradient is consequently steeper and its erosive power thus enhanced.

(*b*) The same results will be produced if the course of the pirate stream runs along a fault or zone of structural weakness.

In many cases both circumstances apply, but there are also good examples in Wales of the individual action of one or the other.

It seems fairly clear that the present-day drainage pattern in Wales has evolved from an original general easterly and south-easterly trend of flow. This direction of drainage into the English Midlands

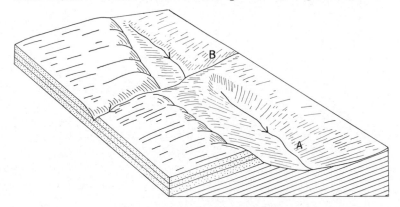

FIG. 51. Imminent river capture.

(After Brown)

FIG. 52. The drainage of Wales with possible wind-gaps numbered.

was thought by Strahan (1902), O. T. Jones (1951) and Linton (1951)
to have been initiated during the early Tertiary Period upon a thin
covering, probably of Cretaceous rock, which sloped gently east
and south-east off the underlying peneplain of Primary rock. As
this thin mantle was removed, so the drainage which originated upon
it became *superimposed* upon the underlying peneplain. This, then,
would be the original direction of Welsh drainage, developed down
the initial general slope. These streams are accordingly termed the
consequents.

One or two examples can be cited here. The headwaters of the
Dee seem to have been in Snowdonia, whence they flowed east-south-
east along the present course of the Llugwy, across the present

Conway, through what is now a wind-gap just west of Cerrigy-drudion, and finally into the present Dee valley at Corwen. The headwaters of the Tywi, flowing south-east from eastern Cardiganshire, probably crossed the present Black Mountain and joined what is now the Cynon-Taff system.

Only remnants of this primeval pattern remain. During the Tertiary Period, a succession of adjustments in base level gave the streams renewed erosive vigour. However, it was those streams which had developed along lines of weakness which were able to make the most efficient use of their new virility. These were the *subsequents*, usually tributaries of the consequents, which, eroding rapidly headward and downwards, have accomplished scores of captures, beheading the consequents and leaving dozens of wind-gaps. Brown (1960) stresses the uncertainty of recognising niches in the skyline as wind-gaps due to capture, but has been able to produce a map showing nearly 100 possible wind-gaps in Wales (Fig. 52).

Thus, it would appear that the present Welsh drainage pattern has been evolved from the original radial east and south-east-flowing consequent pattern by a process of widespread river capture. The process of river capture is not complete, but if the present period of

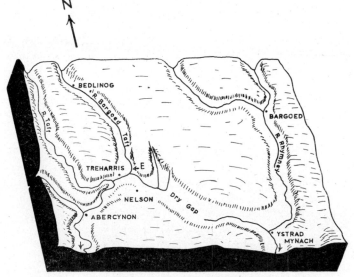

FIG. 53.   Capture of the River Bargoed Taff by a tributary of the River Taff, Glamorgan.

stillstand continues long enough, the lines of structural weakness will dominate the river pattern to an increasing degree. In other words, the original pattern of consequent main rivers with subsequent tributaries will, eventually, be completely reversed. The present stage is intermediate; some of the major rivers are consequents (*e.g.* Taff, Dee, Middle Wye), others subsequents (*e.g.* Conway, Tywi, Upper Severn).

The most spectacular examples of river capture will be those which are most recent in occurrence; the processes of nature will not yet have had sufficient time to mask the obvious characteristics. Some examples of this kind will now be discussed. All have two significant common features: a wind-gap, and a marked change in direction on the part of the captured stream — the 'elbow of capture'.

In the South Wales Coalfield occurs a minor yet striking illustration (Fig. 53). The Bargoed Taff, flowing south-south-eastwards from Bedlinog (154, 0901), is clearly a former tributary of the Rhymni and once flowed into it at Ystrad Mynach (1494). However, a short tributary of the rejuvenated Taff, entering the latter at Treharris (0996), was able to erode headward with sufficient vigour to behead the Rhymni tributary, leaving a wind-gap between Ystrad Mynach and Llancaiach (1196), and an elbow of capture at Trelewis (1097).

Farther west, the fault-lines of the Neath and Tawe valleys have become the dominant drainage lines of West Glamorgan (Fig. 54). The original trend of the major valleys was south-eastwards, as instanced by the obvious alignment of the valleys of the Clydach (tributary to the lower Neath), and the Upper Clydach, which is now a tributary of the Tawe at Pontardawe. Farther north in the same district, a continuation of the Twrch and Gledd valleys leads across a wind-gap into the Dulais valley north of Crynant. It is clear that the Tawe has captured the original consequent streams by virtue of rapid vertical and headward erosion along its fault-line. In other words, the trend of drainage has been altered from its initial consequent direction (south-eastwards) to the former subsequent direction (south-westwards) along the Tawe fault.

In North Wales, the Conway, eroding headward along the faulted junction between the Ordovician sedimentaries and volcanics of Snowdonia on the west and the Silurian series of the Denbighshire Uplands on the east, succeeded in capturing the headwaters of the

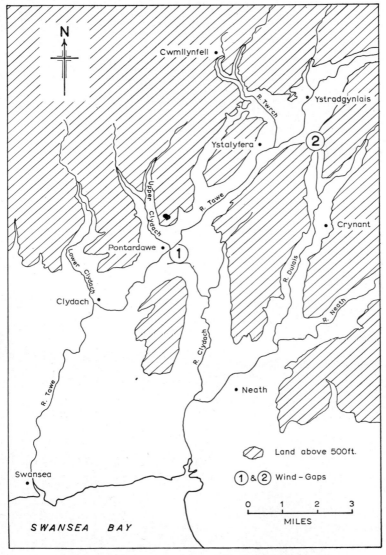

FIG. 54.   Capture of the Rivers Upper Clydach (1) and
Twrch (2), by the River Tawe, Glamorgan.

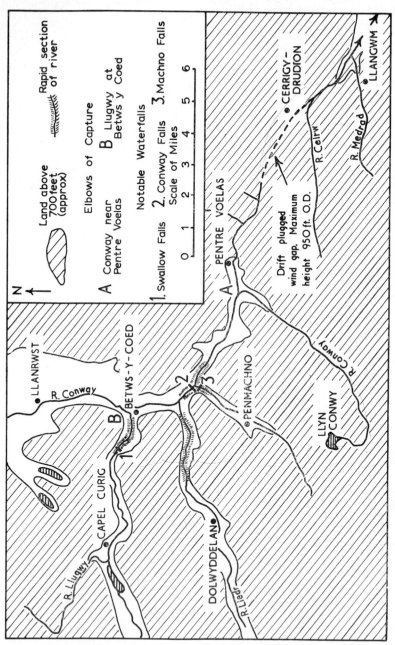

Key (legend):

N

Land above 700 feet (approx)

Rapid section of river

Elbows of Capture
A Conway near Pentre Voelas
B Llugwy at Betws y Coed

Notable Waterfalls
1. Swallow Falls 2. Conway Falls 3. Machno Falls

Scale of Miles
0 1 2 3 4 5 6

LLANRWST
R. Conway
BETWS-Y-COED
B
CAPEL CURIG
R. Llugwy
DOLWYDDELAN
R. Lledr
PENMACHNO
PENTRE VOELAS
A
R. Conway
LLYN CONWY
Drift plugged wind gap. Maximum height 950 ft. O.D.
CERRIGY-DRUDION
R. Ceirw
R. Medrad
LLANGWM

Fig. 55. Capture of the proto-Dee by the River Conway, North Wales.

former Dee at Betws-y-Coed (107, 7956). Further headward erosion south-eastwards along the former Dee valley towards Pentre Voelas resulted in the capture of the stream which now forms the Upper Conway, thus leaving a wind-gap to the east just west of Cerrigydrudion (108, 9548). This wind-gap is simple to detect even on an atlas map, although it has been plugged by considerable thicknesses of glacial drift. The elbows of capture of the Llugwy at Betws-y-Coed and the Conway itself near Pentre Voelas (107, 8551) are equally obvious (Fig. 55).

At Devil's Bridge, Cardiganshire (127, 7477), the Rheidol, eroding headward through a well-marked water-shed, has captured what was probably the Upper Teifi. The famous Rheidol and Mynach Falls represent the drop in level between the former Teifi valley and the present lower Rheidol. Farther south, the Ystwyth has performed a similar function, assisted by the fault-line along which it flows through Pontrhydygroes (7372). South of Devil's Bridge is a remarkable wind-gap, and that south of Ysbyty Ystwyth (7371) is only slightly less so. The alignment between the Upper Rheidol and the Teifi is clear on a large atlas map of Wales, as is the elbow of capture in the Rheidol at Devil's Bridge (Fig. 56). This capture is amongst the most spectacular in Britain, owing to its relatively recent occurrence — probably during an early interglacial or the immediate pre-glacial period.

Many examples can be quoted from other parts of Wales, including in north-east Wales the 300° turn made by the River Alun at Rhydymwyn (108, 2066). This river formerly flowed directly north from its present headwaters through Nannerch (1669), and joined the Clwyd near Bodfari — the present course, in fact, of the Wheeler — but it was captured from the south-east by a tributary of the Dee, leaving a wind-gap at Star Crossing (1767) and a prominent elbow of capture at Rhydymwyn. Right on the Montgomeryshire border with England is the case of the Caebitra, which, eroding headward from the north, beheaded an eastward-flowing consequent at Church Stoke (128, 2794), where the elbow of capture is again in evidence.

Space does not permit consideration of several other outstanding cases of river capture; notably those of the Tywi/Usk and the Neath/Cynon. For detail on these cases the reader is referred to T. N. George (1942), R. O. Jones (1939) and A. Strahan (1902).

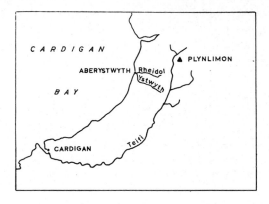

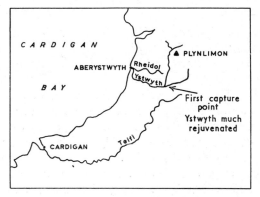

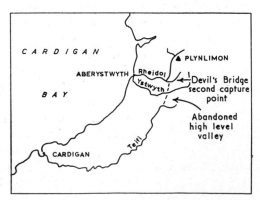

FIG. 56. Capture of the upper Teifi River by the Rheidol and Ystwyth Rivers, Cardiganshire.

ESCARPMENTS

The mode of origin of most sedimentary rocks ensures that they show distinct signs of bedding or stratification, which, in the first instance, was more or less flat and horizontal. Owing to earth-movements, sedimentary beds seldom retain their original horizontal position. Usually they are tilted and the angle at which the general stratification of the rocks inclines from the horizontal is called the *dip*. The dip of the rocks, which may vary from a few degrees to nearly vertical, has a considerable influence on landforms. Denudation will wear away the highest portions of the tilted series, while differential erosion of the hard and soft bands of rock often assists

FIG. 57. The Old Red Sandstone escarpment of the Black Mountains, Brecon. The scarp slope falls away into the Wye valley (*right*) and the strata dip gradually away (*left*) at 2–5°. The escarpment top rises to 2,338 feet at Rhos Dirion (*centre background*).

in the formation of escarpments, since erosion of the soft rocks tends to undermine the harder rocks above them.

The sedimentary strata associated with the South Wales Coalfield are disposed in a broad basin or syncline with a general east-west axis along the Armorican or Hercynian structural trend. Where the strata outcrop along the northern and southern margins, the alternating layers of different hardness are reflected in the stepped character of the landscape. Both the Coal Measures and the Carboniferous Limestone shales are soft and easily eroded and their outcrops generally correspond with depressions or vales; the Pennant Sandstone, Millstone Grit, Carboniferous Limestone and Old Red Sandstone Series, on the other hand, which also outcrop in succession around the Coalfield, are resistant and stand out as asymmetrical uplands (*cuestas*) having gentle dip slopes and steep scarp slopes as escarpments.

Fig. 57 is a view looking south-westwards along the northern face or escarpment of the Black Mountains of Breconshire (not to be confused with the Black Mountain of Carmarthenshire). It shows the gently inclined plateau surface sloping away to the south-south-east (left) at the angle of dip of the rocks of about 2–5°, and the steep descent of the escarpment to the north-west (right) to the lovely valley of the River Wye, some 4 miles away. The edge of the escarpment, formed by the outcrop of a resistant 'cap' of tough grits and conglomerates, exceeds 2,000 feet O.D. at this point, whereas the lower ground of the Wye valley, made up of marls and sandstones, is no more than about 300 feet O.D. The valley of the River Usk in the distance and beyond the Black Mountains separates them from the Brecon Beacons, the long dip slope of which is visible on the horizon. Beyond the Beacons this prominent outer northern escarpment of the Old Red Sandstone Series can be traced westwards along the northern edge of Fforest Fawr and the Black Mountain.

In North Wales, the impressive wall-like slope rising above the valleys of the Eglwyseg and Dee to the bare white crags of Creigiau Eglwyseg (Eglwyseg Mountain) (Fig. 58) is another fine example of an escarpment. In this case, it is the hard Carboniferous Limestone which forms the pronounced relief feature while the softer Ludlow shales of the Silurian series form the low ground (Fig. 59).

The *scree* slopes at the foot of the escarpment are a feature of most upland areas in temperate latitudes where much bare rock is exposed. In winter when water freezes within the interstices of a

FIG. 58. The Eglwyseg Mountain, Denbigh. This escarpment of Carboniferous Limestone is a well-known scenic feature which dominates the approach to the Horse Shoe Pass from Llangollen.

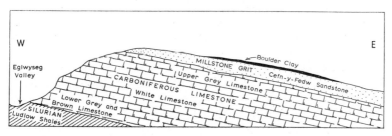

FIG. 59. Geological section of Eglwyseg Mountain, Denbigh.

rock, its volume increases by about 10 per cent, thus exercising great pressure. Repetition of this process many times causes the rock to shatter and fragments to fall. Such heaps of angular fragments, piled at the steepest possible angle of rest, slip and move each time new fragments fall on them. They are extremely treacherous to the climber who inadvertently disturbs the precarious state of equilibrium. The walls of the glaciated valleys of Snowdonia are typically footed by scree slopes, as is the north face of the Cadair Idris escarpment (p. 24, Fig. 24).

F

The presence of many 'dead' screes in Wales suggests that most were formed during colder times at the close of the glacial epoch, when the temperature fluctuated around freezing point for long periods.

SUPERIMPOSED DRAINAGE

The rocks which form the land surface at the present time are generally not those that were exposed at the surface when the area was uplifted from beneath the sea. Agents of erosion, over millions of years, have removed the original surface cover to expose underlying rocks. The drainage system, however, often originated in accord with the structure of the original overlying land surface and what we now have is a *superimposed* pattern and likely to be ill-adapted to the underlying strata. The rivers of Wales, for instance, form part of an original radial drainage pattern probably formed on Cretaceous rocks associated with a main water parting running from Snowdon through Merioneth and Cardiganshire to Pembrokeshire. However, as a result of subsequent erosion along belts of weakness, river capture, earth-movements and glaciation, the overall motif of the present drainage pattern is one of considerable complexity.

Superimposition of drainage can sometimes lead to most unexpected results. The Taff gorge at Taff's Well is a good example. The River Taff flows, by this gorge, straight through the upturned strata of the border ridges or south crop of the South Wales Coalfield, just north of Cardiff. It was thought by Strahan that the Taff, like other rivers in south-east Wales, was initiated upon a surface of Upper Cretaceous rocks which was inclined towards the south and south-east. In time these strata were removed by denudation with the rivers eroding through them to reach the older foundation strata below. However, the southerly trend of the rivers was maintained and they became superimposed on to the complex geological structures of the coal-basin to which they bear no relation.

The view (Fig. 60) is that of the Taff gorge looking north-eastwards across the South Wales Coalfield towards the Brecon Beacons on the skyline. The village of Tongwynlais, the northern limit of Cardiff's suburbia, is in the right foreground, Taff's Well lies beyond the viaduct and beyond again are the Nantgarw Colliery, coke ovens and by-product plant and the Trefforest Industrial Estate. The Taff, flowing from the north, passes first through the

FIG. 60. The Taff gorge between Nantgarw and Tongwynlais (*right foreground*). The Nantgarw Colliery and Trefforest Industrial Estate are in the left background and the Brecon Beacons are visible on the skyline. The gorge is cut across a ridge of Carboniferous Limestone and Old Red Sandstone upon which is built the castle, Castell Coch (*foreground*).

wide flat-floored valley containing the Industrial Estate. It then cuts straight across resistant and steeply dipping Pennant grits of the east-west ridge which rises to 1,009 feet in the Garth Hill (left centre). A slight widening of the valley follows at Taff's Well as a result of differential erosion acting upon softer Lower Coal Series strata and the action of strike streams, only to be followed by a pronounced constriction to a mere 500 yards between Taff's Well and Tongwynlais where the valley is hemmed in by the steep walls of the west-east aligned ridge of Carboniferous Limestone and Old Red Sandstone which rises to 587 feet in the Little Garth (left foreground). The Taff then debouches on to the coastal plain to enter the sea at Cardiff. The route through this gorge provides the main outlet for the coals and the products of a variety of light industries from the Rhondda-Taff-Cynon group of valleys to the north.

The ridge across which the Taff has cut the gorge is itself worthy of mention. The escarpment form resulting from differential erosion of inclined strata has already been noted (p. 61). The nearer the rocks are to the horizontal, the more nearly will the landform be plateau-like in character. When the strata are inclined at a steep angle, however, the scarp-slope and dip-slope of the escarpment are likely to have similar gradients. A feature of this kind is known as a *hog's back*, typified by the famous Hog's Back between Farnham and Guildford in Surrey. The ridge in the illustration (Fig. 57), however, is equally typical. The Old Red Sandstone strata dip away northwards at angles of between 40 and 60° (compare the gentle dip — 2–5° — of the rocks along the north crop). Farther east (*i.e.* to the right) the same ridge becomes Caerphilly Mountain, overlooking the northern suburbs of Cardiff, with equally steep descents into Caerphilly on the north and Cardiff on the south.

The same type of hog's back ridge, similarly punctured by gorges, recurs sporadically right along the southern fringe of the coalfield in Glamorgan and Monmouth. The Rhymni near Machen (154, 2189) and the Ebbw near Risca (2390) cut through the same strata as the Taff at Taff's Well. Farther west, the feature is frequently accorded the name *cefn*, Cefn Hirgoed (154, 9482) and Cefn Cribwr (153, 8683) being outstanding examples. The Ogmore, also superimposed, cuts through the ridge formed by these two at Aberkenfig. Cefn Cribwr is the more striking and runs westwards for three miles from Aberkenfig to Kenfig Hill (8383).

LIMESTONE (KARST) SCENERY

Some parts of Wales have been shown to owe their landforms and scenery to igneous rocks of varied types. In fact, all rock types produce relief features with a certain degree of individuality. But apart from igneous rocks only the compact or crystalline limestone (as distinct from the soft limestone or chalk which is absent in Wales) gives rise to landforms worthy of special mention.

The limestones of Wales are well-jointed sedimentary rocks, composed essentially of calcium carbonate. Unlike most rocks they are readily soluble in rain-water charged with carbon dioxide after its passage through the atmosphere. Solubility combined with permeability along the joints and bedding-planes means that such slightly acid water, instead of flowing in streams over the surface, quickly makes its way downwards through joints and along bedding-planes.

On its way the water dissolves the limestone and channels are enlarged to permit water to pass along them. In this way fissures and caverns are formed, which may eventually become large enough to carry all the water that would normally flow at the surface. Thus limestone areas are often characterised by an absence of surface drainage, with streams disappearing into fissures or swallow (*sink*) holes, features such as dry stream-beds and caverns and a land surface which is sometimes bare or else carries only a thin soil cover. Since running water at the surface is at a minimum, surface erosion is

FIG. 61. The Great Orme, Llandudno, Caernarvonshire. The toll road, much used by summer visitors, is cut into the headland of Carboniferous Limestone (*right*).

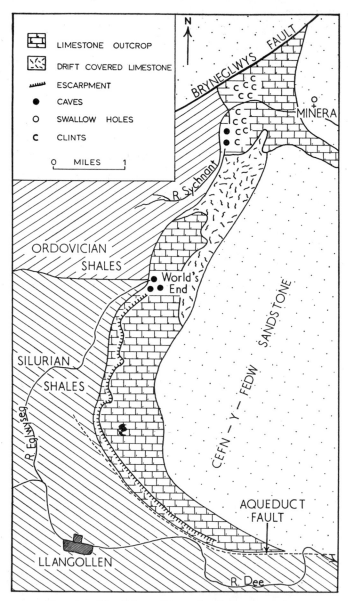

FIG. 62. The Minera–Llangollen limestone region.

limited and consequently this type of limestone not infrequently forms high ground. Disappearing streams may emerge at the foot of a steep slope, especially at the sides of main valleys incised below the water table. Such reappearances are known as *Vauclusian* issues, after the famous Fontaine de Vaucluse in southern France.

A familiar landmark and quite typical example of limestone scenery is the impressive headland of the Great Orme, Llandudno (Fig. 61). This landform is developed out of well-stratified and

FIG. 63. Swallow holes in Millstone Grit (overlying Carboniferous Limestone) on Mynydd Llangynidr, Breconshire, north-west of Ebbw Vale. Approximate scale of air photograph 1 inch equals 1,250 feet.

FIG. 64. Dry stream-bed of the River Heps
near Ystradfellte, Breconshire.

FIG. 65. Weathered limestone surface near Pontsticill on the
Glamorgan–Brecon boundary.

well-jointed Carboniferous Limestone. The absence of surface
water, the outcrop of bare rock from beneath a thin soil cover and
wall-like precipices are clearly visible on this view looking westward.

Halkyn Mountain, Ruabon Mountain and the Eglwyseg Moors

in north-east Wales all illustrate typical limestone scenery in greater
or lesser degree. The Eglwyseg Mountain, Llangollen (Fig. 58), is a
massive escarpment of Carboniferous Limestone, while the Minera–
Llangollen region (Fig. 62) abounds in swallow holes, clints and
caves.

In South Wales the comparatively wide exposure of Carboniferous
Limestone beyond the north crop of the coalfield provides a
fascinating array of limestone forms. For 30 miles from the Twrch
valley (153, 7614) in south-east Carmarthenshire, through the head
of the Tawe valley to the headwaters of the Neath and eastwards to
Mynydd Llangynidr, Mynydd Llangatwg and Blorenge (141, 2611),
the Carboniferous Limestone country, over 1,000 feet above sea-level,
is closely pocked with innumerable small, medium and large swallow
holes (Fig. 63). These circular depressions mostly mark the sites
of underground caverns of which the roofs have collapsed. Even
where the limestone is overlain by a relatively thin covering of
Millstone Grit its presence is indicated by swallow holes occurring
within the Grit after the collapse of the limestone beneath. The
total area affected by swallow holes in all this region is some 15,000
acres, of which some 6,000 acres are located on the Grit outcrops.
Elsewhere in this area, dry river courses (Fig. 64), weathered
limestone surfaces with little soil (Fig. 65), caves, caverns and
limestone 'scars' abound and there are innumerable points where
surface drainage is seen to disappear, as, for instance, at Porth-yr-
Ogof (141, 927123) on Afon Mellte in Brecon.

Fig. 66 shows a vertical aerial view of typical limestone country
near the northern end of the Tawe valley. The photograph clearly
depicts the dry valley leading down to the famous Dan-yr-Ogof caves
(153, 8316) near Craig-y-Nos. The emergence of the stream at the
mouth of the caves can be cited as a fine Welsh example of a
Vauclusian issue. Other features of note are the swallow holes of
varying sizes, the north end of the Cribarth Ridge (bottom right),
and the limestone pavements in which the major joint direction is
north-east to south-west.

Along the south coast of Gower (p. 130), Carboniferous Limestone is exposed in magnificent cliffs. Here the rock gives rise to
some of the finest coastal scenery in Wales. The strata are inclined
steeply away from the sea and are cut up into coves and headlands
(Fig. 107). The small coves are eroded along joints or lines of
weakness within the strata and there are numerous small sea-caves

Fig. 66. Limestone country near Craig-y-Nos, Brecon, showing the dry valley leading down to the famous Dan-yr-Ogof caves (*left centre*). Craig-y-Nos castle can also be seen (*top right*). Approximate scale of air photograph 4½ inches to

excavated in the cliff face. No less impressive are the Carboniferous Limestone cliffs of South Pembrokeshire between Stackpole (151, 9994) and Linney Head (Fig. 108).

GLACIAL FEATURES

The glaciation of Wales began something under 1 million years ago, in the Pleistocene Period of Quaternary times, and followed a very long period of both river and marine erosion. The striking nature of the present-day glacial landforms is a result of their comparative youth ; the last glaciers retreated as man began to emerge from his primeval state, geologically speaking very recently. During the Ice Age, temperatures were lowered generally by about 20° F., though the drop was probably greater in the winter. This may not seem a sufficiently marked drop in temperature to produce an ice age of the scale experienced, but it should be borne in mind that it was the copiousness of the snowfall rather than the actual degree of coldness which caused the vast accumulations of ice that transformed the Welsh landscape so profoundly.

The cause of this lowering of temperature is uncertain ; however, it seems apparent that the areas which received the most copious snowfall are those same areas which today experience heavy 'relief' rainfall (that is, rain caused by onshore prevailing winds being forced to rise over mountains or hills adjacent to the coast). In Wales, therefore, the heaviest snow-caps developed upon the higher western ranges — Plynlimon, Cadair Idris, the Rhinogs and, in particular, Snowdonia — whereas those of the ranges farther east were a good deal smaller. In fact, evidence shows that the Radnor Forest had no ice-cap of its own, but was glaciated up to a considerable height by ice from sources to the west as it moved eastwards into the Midlands (Fig. 67).

These Welsh mountain ice-caps typify the *first* universally recognised type of glaciation, namely *mountain* or *valley glaciation*. Snowfall in mountainous areas accumulates in the valleys, where it becomes compressed into ice by the weight of the fresh snow supplied from above. Such conditions exist today in many of the higher fold ranges in the world — in the Himalayas, Alps, Rockies, Andes and the New Zealand Alps, and they result in the features known as

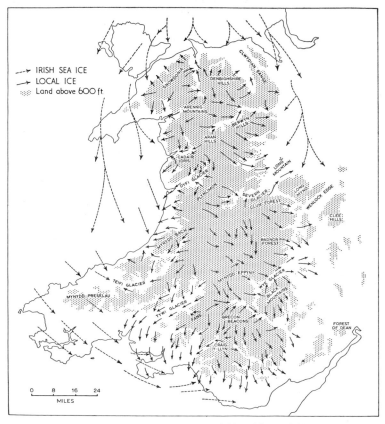

IRISH SEA ICE
LOCAL ICE
Land above 600 ft

(Adapted from British Regional Geology)

FIG. 67.   The glaciation of Wales.

cirques, hanging valleys, U-shaped valleys, arêtes and ribbon lakes. It must be stressed, however, that the work of these valley glaciers in Wales, as elsewhere, was largely directed by the pattern of deeply-entrenched river valleys which was already in existence prior to the onset of the ice. The effect of the glaciation was thus to modify or alter this set of river-moulded landforms; it transformed the *details* of the landscape and produced features of great splendour. It is no coincidence that the most famous areas of inland beauty in Britain are the geographer's favourite hunting-grounds for examples of glacial erosion — Snowdonia, the Lake District and the Scottish Highlands. In these areas, the former young river valleys were straightened and their bases widened. Hundreds of lakes (of several types) reflect the uneven erosion of the ice; the heads of the valleys were accentuated, frequently becoming steep and precipitous. Soil patiently evolved and stratified by Nature over thousands of years was extensively stripped and deposited elsewhere, mixed with stones and boulders, pebbles and gravel, which rendered it useless or discouraging to the farmer.

A second source of ice must also be accounted for, namely the Irish Sea *ice-sheet*. In the depression of the Irish Sea, ice accumulated from the mountains of Scotland, Ireland and the Isle of Man, and this sheet became so powerful that it impinged upon the North Wales coast and encroached upon the lower slopes of northern Snowdonia, where it reached heights of over 1,500 feet. The force of the local Welsh ice moving off the mountains of North Wales, however, split the Irish Sea ice into two 'wings', one of which crossed Anglesey and Llŷn into Cardigan Bay, the other branching south-east on to the Cheshire Plain and into North Shropshire, where it dammed the waters of the middle Severn (which then flowed into the Dee), and diverted them south-east through what is now the Ironbridge gorge.

In Cardigan Bay, the western arm of the Irish Sea ice piled up great quantities of debris against the coastal cliffs, forming platforms which are now rapidly being removed by the erosion of the sea. Extensive fragments, however, remain between Llannon and Llanrhystyd (Cardiganshire). In the Bristol Channel, this ice blocked the exits of many of the rivers and resulted in a series of overflow channels, usually running west-east, which have been invaluable in the development of the communications system of South Wales. It also carried 'erratics' from Pembrokeshire as far east as Cardiff.

The effects of this sheet of ice which spread into Wales from the surrounding seas were less spectacular than those of valley glaciation, and it is true to say that it is the indirect effects (*i.e.* the overflow channels and allied features) which are the most immediately apparent. Nevertheless, the Irish Sea ice exemplifies the *second* recognised type of glaciation, namely *sheet glaciation*. During the Ice Age, ice enveloped considerable areas of territory which sometimes attained continental proportions, as, for example, in the cases of the Canadian and Baltic Shield areas, both of which were covered by vast ice-sheets of great thickness. However, in these latter areas, the extraordinary age and resistance of the rocks have caused the *erosional* effects of the ice-sheet to be dominant, whereas in those parts of Wales affected by the Irish Sea ice, features resulting from glacial *deposition* are both more widespread and more prominent.

Landforms characteristic of the Canadian North are, however, found in certain areas of very limited extent in the Welsh Uplands, on plateaux such as Y Migneint (North Merioneth), where the ice succeeded in burying the whole landscape and not merely the valleys and depressions. Inevitably, the rock-knobs, lakes and marshes produced by this type of plateau glaciation are all much smaller than their counterparts in the Canadian and Baltic Shield regions. They nevertheless illustrate the wide differences which exist between a glaciated landscape which was *completely buried* by an ice-sheet, and the glaciated hill or mountain country where the glaciers gravitated into and moved down the *valleys* and hollows.

GLACIATED VALLEYS

All the major Welsh valleys were glaciated during the Ice Age. The former young river valleys were straightened and over-deepened, and their bases were widened. Enormous quantities of ice moved down them, and sometimes the congestion was so great in areas of ice accumulation that glaciers over-rode the water-shed into the next valley system. In many cases, the valley glacier was sufficiently persistent to press on below the snow-line even though the surrounding high ground had lost its snow cover. This was true of the Dee in the Llangollen area and the lower Ogwen valleys of North Wales, and the lower Tawe and Neath in South Wales.

Former youthful river valleys lost their interlocking spurs as the ice ground through on its inexorable course. The V-shaped pre-glacial cross-section became U-shaped, and what is often no more than a small brook meanders across the floor of an enormous glaciated trough (Fig. 68). The sides of the valley are exceedingly steep, and landslides are common as loose weathered material becomes too much for the slope it rests upon. The smooth long profile of the river valley, often corresponding to a logarithmic curve, becomes very irregular as the glacier excavates rock basins (Fig. 69), and this sometimes results in ribbon lakes. Any irregularity in the river profile (such as a knickpoint) is further accentuated by the glacier, and the rapids become a waterfall, known as a *talschluss*. The head of the valley is also exaggerated and made steeper, often resulting in a complete 'dead-end' or cul-de-sac for communications and commonly termed *blaen* (pl. *blaenau*) in Welsh place-names, *e.g.* Blaen Rhondda. Small tributaries cascade down the towering valley sides from *hanging valleys* high above.

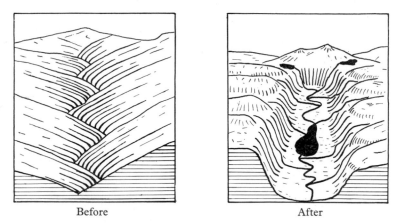

Before   After

FIG. 68. River valley before and after glaciation.

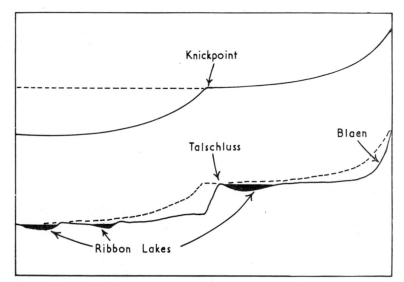

FIG. 69. Long profile of river valley before and after glaciation.

No Welsh valley exhibits all these features, but Nant Ffrancon, or Dyffryn Ogwen, which carries the A5 London–Holyhead road south-eastwards from Bethesda in Caernarvonshire, comes very close to being a classic example (Fig. 70). Its cross-section shows a perfect 'U', its sides are extremely steep, and landslides are a common hazard in wet weather. Moreover, the tributaries on either side, such as Cwm Perfedd and Cwm Ceunant on the south-west and Afon Berthen on the north-east, tumble over 1,000 feet down into the main valley, and are fine instances of hanging valleys. However, the steep back wall or 'blaen' so characteristic of the South Wales valleys is not present, because the volume of ice accumulating in the Llyn Ogwen region from Cwm Idwal (107, 6459), Cwm Bochlwyd (6559) and Cwm Lloer (6662) was so excessive that the former water-shed at Rhaeadr Ogwen (6460) was breached. Nevertheless, the steepness of the drop of 300 feet at Rhaeadr Ogwen is typical of the sudden termination of most glacial valley heads. The drop itself probably represents a former knickpoint which receded beneath an ice-fall until its recession was arrested by a more resistant outcrop. It is thus a form of 'talschluss'. Nant Ffrancon is one of the very few major glaciated valleys in the Snowdonia National Park which contain no ribbon lake. The evidence strongly suggests, however, that the stretch of flat floor in the upper part of the valley between Ty-gwyn (642627) and Rhaeadr Ogwen is the former site of one, which became rapidly filled up with sediment brought in by the overloaded river and its tributaries.

Almost every locality in Wales can produce its own examples of glaciated valleys. The Tawe and Neath valleys show ample signs of glaciation, and it has been shown that the rock-floor of the lower Tawe in the last 2 miles has been excavated over 100 feet below the present sea-level. The valleys of the Berwyns show excellent glacial forms, Cwm Pennant (117, 0325) in the upper Tanat valley, near Llangynog, being a superb example. Other fine instances are the Honddu valley in the Brecon Beacons (141, 2434), and Cwm Tryweryn (116, 8540), north-west of Bala, which is being dammed at a narrow point about 5 miles from Bala to augment the water supply of Merseyside. The scheme began supplying water in 1965.

There are several characteristics of glaciated valleys which are sufficiently important to be considered individually; these are hanging valleys, ribbon lakes and the 'blaen', or trough's end.

Fig. 70. Nant Ffrancon, Caernarvonshire, a classic Welsh example of a glaciated valley. The Penrhyn Quarries at Bethesda are in the centre background, with the trunk road A5 leading down Nant Ffrancon from the head of Llyn Ogwen (*right centre*).

G

HANGING VALLEYS

These occur where the main valley is excavated at a rate which was not maintained in the tributary valleys. As a result, the tributary streams now emerge at a level high above the main floor, to which they descend by means of long waterfalls and rapids. The simplest explanation for this deeper excavation of the main valley is that it had the larger and more powerful glacier, but it is possible that the over-deepening of the main valley by comparison with its tributary was accomplished in some cases by the rapid down-cutting of stream erosion in the main valley in an interglacial period, during which the higher surrounding slopes were deprived of water by the frigid conditions. In this case, the subsequent resumption of glacial erosion would restore the 'U' shape of the main valley. Hanging valleys are usually found in profusion along the sides of any deep glaciated valley. In most Welsh examples, the catchment areas are very small, and their flow is consequently erratic. Frequently their courses are dry, but, following heavy rain, vertical white ribbons of foaming water are a common sight in the Welsh mountains.

Nant Bwa Drain (Fig. 71 (127, 7179)) provides a striking illustration of the *form* of a hanging valley and is frequently quoted as a classic example. It is doubtful, however, whether its mode of origin is in any way typical. The stream has succeeded in cutting a considerable niche into the glaciated valley-side; the most spectacular erosion accomplished by the stream is, therefore, plainly *post-glacial*. Accordingly, it is likely that the entry of Nant Bwa Drain into the Rheidol here is itself a post-glacial phenomenon, and that before the Ice Age the tributary entered the Rheidol as much as a mile or more upstream, since its direction of flow is, in fact, south-east until it turns and plunges into the Rheidol. Moreover, the pre-glacial Rheidol was already deeply incised into the plateau, and the difference in altitude between the valley bottom and the present knickpoint of Nant Bwa Drain was already considerable. It would thus appear that the 'hanging' form of Nant Bwa Drain is not in any substantial degree dependent upon differential glacial deepening as between main valley and tributary.

More typical is the succession of hanging streams descending the western side of Nant Ffrancon (Fig. 70), notably Cwm Ceunant (107, 6263) and Cwm Perfedd. These have not, so far, incised themselves into the valley-side save for a small niche which Afon

FIG. 71. Nant Bwa Drain, Cardiganshire. This 'hanging' tributary drops
over 600 feet in under half a mile to the River Rheidol below. A
short distance downstream (*left of the photograph*) is the generating station
of the Rheidol Hydro-Electric Scheme.

Perfedd has cut into some boulder clay at its base.   Other examples of hanging valleys can be found on both sides of the Vale of Ewyas (141, 2630), Cwm Lluest (154, 9199) at the upper end of the Rhondda valley, Nant Cawrddu (108, 0841) and Nant Llechog (0941) in the Dee valley, Nant Graig Wen near Dinas Mawddwy in the Aran range (116, 8318), and Cwm Dyli in the Snowdon massif, where the fall from Llyn Llydaw is utilised in the generation of hydro-electric power at 653539.   Hundreds of other examples abound all over the Welsh mountains.

RIBBON LAKES

Ribbon lakes are, in Wales, a stringent test of the severity of ice erosion, for it is only those areas of most drastic valley glaciation which possess this feature; none is found outside Merioneth and Caernarvon, and in the former county, only two examples may be pointed out.   The vast majority are thus in Caernarvonshire, where a profusion of ribbon lakes is found at two levels.

The origin of this feature is largely dependent upon the property possessed by ice enabling it to excavate rock-basins, and flow 'uphill', as it were, out of them.   There seems to be a marked correspondence in North Wales, as elsewhere, between the locations of ribbon lakes and either a region of ice accumulation or a constriction of the valley sides.   In either case, the excavating power of the ice is enhanced.   Llyn Tegid is illustrative of both factors, whereas Llyn Cwellyn, 3 miles west of Snowdon, presents a fine instance of constriction in front of the lake, beneath Craig Cwmbychan (107, 5455).   Tal-y-llyn (Fig. 6) clearly illustrates constriction of the valley sides, and is the southernmost ribbon lake in Britain.

The most striking example which can be considered in Snowdonia is provided by the lake which has now been split into the twin lakes Padarn and Peris (Fig. 41).   The sudden arrest of the speed of the heavily-loaded Afon Arddu led to a deltaic deposition which has succeeded in spreading right across the former width of the lake. The shape of Llyn Peris has been altered by man, too; extensive quarry-waste dumpings have taken place on the north-eastern side of the lake.   Llyn Peris is 1,930 yards long (Jehu, 1902), and has an average breadth of 310 yards.   Its average depth is 63·9 feet, and the maximum depth of 114 feet is attained in two places near the lower end of the lake.   The maximum depth of Llyn Padarn is near its upper end; it is larger but shallower than Peris, having an average depth of 52·4 feet and a maximum of 94 feet. The location of the deepest water in the two lakes (near the central alluvial area), together with the difference in level between them of only 0·1 feet, tend to confirm that Padarn and Peris are, in fact, the result of the splitting of a single lake. Jehu concluded that the presence of alluvial tracts as far down the valley as Cwm-y-Glo and as far up as Gwastadnant indicates a much larger original ribbon lake almost 5 miles long.

Llyn Padarn and Llyn Peris belong to the second of two groups of ribbon lakes found in Snowdonia. These two groups are the shallow lakes, typified by Ogwen and Idwal, with maximum depths of 10 feet and 36 feet respectively, and the deep lakes, examples being Cowlyd and Cwellyn. These same two categories have also been recognised in the Lake District, Derwentwater and Bassenthwaite (18 feet mean depth) exemplifying the first type and Crummock Water, Buttermere, Coniston and Ullswater the second.

The ribbon lakes of Snowdonia have developed in rock-basins, and it is unusual to find any morainic damming having contributed substantially to their depth, except in the case of some of the higher ones, where the catchment area is small and the volume of outflow slight. In the case of Llyn Llydaw, a dam of morainic material is responsible for an additional 40–50 feet of depth, and Llyn Idwal is also moraine-impounded. The levels of the lower ribbon lakes, however, are unaffected by morainic blockages, since they have copious outflows capable of rapidly cutting down through any such obstruction.

Outside Snowdonia, there are one or two examples of moraine-dammed lakes, but in each case the outflow is small and has been incapable hitherto of reducing the outlet level substantially. The best example is the Talley lakes of Carmarthenshire (140, 6333), impounded by a morainic dam across the valley at Talley, and split into two by another boulder clay mass. Most moraine-dammed lakes in South and Mid-Wales have long since disappeared, the best example of this being Cors Goch Glan Teifi, north of Tregaron (140, 6759). This large area of bog is the remains of two large lakes impounded behind a morainic bar at Tregaron, which, however, soon drained as the outlet level was lowered by the post-glacial Teifi. Llangors Lake (141, 1326), near Brecon, demonstrates an intermediate stage. Partially dammed by the plugging of the valley leading northward by glacial and other gravel, and partly the result of over-deepening, this lake, it is clear, has shrunk to less than half its former extent, a history to which the extensive area between 500 and 510 feet O.D. north of the lake bears eloquent witness.

BLAEN (BLAENAU)

'Blaen' is a name frequently applied to the topographical cul-de-sac in which many glaciated valleys end. Roads either come to an end or they must climb over the steep back wall, as, for instance, the Rhigos and Bwlch-y-Clawdd main roads which climb out of the Rhondda valley towards Hirwaun and Nantymoel respectively. In the densely peopled valleys of the South Wales Coalfield, 'blaen' is frequently used as a prefix to the name of a river to provide the name of the valley-head town, e.g. Blaenrhondda (154, 9200), Blaengwynfi (8996) and Blaenclydach (9893). In the rural districts of Wales, numerous farms are named in this same manner, as, for instance, Blaen Ceulan in Cardiganshire (127, 7190) and Blaen-rhiwarth (117, 9220), beneath the Bala-Llangynog mountain road as it climbs through the Berwyn mountains. Other excellent examples are Blaen Senni (141, 9119), Blaen Olchon (2733), at Foel Blaen Rhisglog (140, 6946) and the end of the Lledr valley in Caernarvonshire above Nhadog Isaf (107, 6850). Fig. 72 depicts a fine instance of the adoption of the term 'blaen' in its plural form. The illustration clearly shows several indentations of the rear valley wall, giving several 'blaenau'; hence the name Blaenau Ffestiniog. The origin of the name 'Ffestiniog' is not so clear, however, and is still the subject of much discussion.

CIRQUES (CORRIES)

It would be difficult to imagine a more characteristic glaciated landform than the cirque. These huge, crater-like, semi-circular or 'armchair-shaped' depressions with precipitous rocky walls up to 1,500 feet high, and often (not always, however) floored by a deep lake, contribute greatly to the shape of many of our higher mountains, particularly Snowdon and Cadair Idris, whose majestic shapes owe a great deal to the sculpture of corrie glaciers.

Most of these corrie glaciers were (at least during the later stages) confined to the head of a tributary valley, where they gathered

FIG. 72. Blaenau Ffestiniog, Merioneth. The Vale of Ffestiniog ends
northwards in this complex of topographical 'dead-ends', hence the
term 'Blaenau'. The Crimea Pass (*left background*) carries the A496
Llandudno–Maentwrog main road, above which towers Moel Siabod
(2,860 feet). Cwm Bowydd (*right foreground*) shows prominent
glaciated characteristics.

in depressions or hollows. They must often have been of insignificant size compared with the mighty ice-flows down the main valleys
of the Principality, but small as they were, their effects were most
striking. The exact mode of origin of the cirque form is still not
absolutely clear, and treatment of the several theories which have
been put forward is beyond the scope of this book. Interested
readers are, however, referred to standard textbooks such as those
by Wooldridge and Morgan (1959) or Sparks (1960). One well-
known theory, which is the basis of many more recent hypotheses,
was put forward by Willard Johnson over fifty years ago, and involves
the break-up of rock by a freeze-thaw process known as 'basal
sapping' at the bottom of a large crack or crevasse found at the rear
of contemporary corrie glaciers, and known as the *bergschrund*.
Johnson's original theory obviously requires modification, since few
contemporary bergschrunds exceed 200 feet in depth, whereas the
rear wall of Cwm Cau on Cadair Idris is 1,500 feet high. The

bergschrund hypothesis has, however, provided an important starting-point for subsequent investigation, and a related process may be responsible for the formation of the 'talschluss' and the 'blaen', both of which have already been referred to.

Corrie glaciers terminated abruptly at the front of their respective hollows, and here they frequently laid down a moraine, which, however, has only rarely had any substantial effect upon the lake level. Most Welsh corries contain lakes, but this is by no means universal, Cwm Saerbren (154, 9397) behind Treherbert and Graig Fawr (9296) behind Cwmparc being fine instances of cirques without lakes. Most Welsh cirques now discharge streams which emerge in valleys hanging high above the main valley floor, *e.g.* Llyn Fawr (154, 9103) and Llyn Fach (9003).

Cirques are profuse in Snowdonia, Cadair Idris and the Rhinog Range, where they are found on all sides of the massifs. Farther south, however, they are confined to the colder north-facing slopes, where the ice lingered longest. In the south the climate was a little warmer, and so cirques were excavated only where conditions were particularly favourable. Thus Llyn Llygad Rheidol (127, 7987) beneath Plynlimon, Llyn y Fan Fawr (140, 8321) and Llyn y Fan

FIG. 73. Llyn Dulyn, in the Carneddau range, Caernarvonshire, surrounded by cliff-like walls and characterising the 'corrie' form.

Fach (8021) on the north face of the Black Mountain in western Breconshire and eastern Carmarthenshire, and Llyn Cwm Llwch (141, 0022) on the Brecon Beacons are all very good examples of cirques ; yet they are isolated examples and not part of a profusion.

The use of the word *corrie* to describe the cirque form in Scotland has tempted many teachers and important writers to use the Welsh word *cwm* for the landform in Wales. This is invalid, for the cirque form is a highly individual one, unique, in fact, to the degree that the use of the broader term 'cwm' cannot be justified. While it is true that most Welsh cirques carry the name 'cwm', the reverse is obviously not the case, and large numbers of 'cymoedd' might be quoted in Wales which do not remotely resemble the cirque form. The Welsh term 'cwm' is applied to any deep valley, and it is unfortunate that it has become identified with the much more restricted 'cirque'.

One of Snowdonia's deepest lakes, Llyn Dulyn (Fig. 73) offers a superb example. It is situated beneath a semicircular precipice between Foel Grach and Foel Fras at 1,747 feet O.D. on the north-east shoulder of the Carneddau range. The almost perpendicular cliffs at the rear end of the lake, seen clearly in the illustration, vary between 500 and 1,000 feet above the lake level, and the evidence shows that this steep drop is continued into the lake, for, beneath these cliffs, Jehu recorded a depth sounding of 55 feet, only 3 feet from the shore. All the sides are rocky except on the east (*i.e.* on the right side of the picture) where a thin veneer of boulder clay underlies the steep grassy slope. The outlet, however, is over bare rock, so the boulder clay has not contributed to the depth of the lake. The maximum depth obtained was 189 feet near the centre, and the average depth 104 feet; the slope to the bottom is thus steep from all sides, but is especially so beneath the cliffs on the west side.

Other examples in Snowdonia include Ffynnon Lloer (107, 6662) and Ffynnon Llugwy (6962) on the southern slopes of the Carneddau, Glaslyn (6154) hewn into the east face of Snowdon, Marchlyn Mawr (6261 — a good example of a moraine-dammed corrie lake), and Llyn Stwlan (6644) near Blaenau Ffestiniog. In the Rhinogs can be found Llyn Du (116, 6529), Llyn Hywel and Llyn y Bi (6626) and Llyn Bodlyn (6424), and on the Cadair Idris range are the two remarkable examples Llyn Cau and Llyn y Gadair (7013). Often quoted as a classic British example, Llyn Cau has a maximum depth of 163 feet (Howe and Yates, 1953), and is surrounded by towering cliffs which reach 1,500 feet above the lake level at Penygadair (2,927 feet O.D.). The deep cwm follows the course of a pre-glacial tributary eroded along a belt of Llyn Cau mudstones, a line of weakness by comparison with the igneous rocks of the Cadair Idris escarpment itself (Fig. 23). Some morainic material is present at the head of the lake, but it is only a thin veneer, through which *roches moutonnées* protrude, and is unlikely to have been responsible for any extra depth in the lake.

An interesting feature of Welsh cirques is their property of occurring in pairs of similar location; note for instance Ffynnon Lloer and Ffynnon Llugwy, Dulyn and Melynllyn, Llyn y Fan Fawr and Llyn y Fan Fach, and Llyn Fawr and Llyn Fach in Glamorgan.

Since tributary valleys ending in cirques usually emerge high above the main valley floor, they obviously represent substantial hydro-electric potential. At Cwm Dyli Power Station (107, 654539) a fall of over 1,000 feet is utilised, while a new scheme at Blaenau Ffestiniog involves the adaptation of Llyn Stwlan as the upper of two reservoirs in a pumped storage scheme. The lower reservoir has been provided by the construction of a dam across Afon Ystradau (107, or 116, 6844), and power is generated by the 800-foot head of water in the usual way during peak periods, the capacity being 300 megawatts. The scheme was completed in 1963.

Surplus power from Trawsfynydd Nuclear Power Station in off-peak periods is used to pump the water back up to Stwlan from the lower Ystradau reservoir. A similar scheme originally conceived to use another corrie-lake (Llyn Cau) as upper reservoir and Tal-y-llyn as the lower one was shelved owing to local opposition.

Arêtes (Cribau)

An *arête*, commonly termed *crib* or *cribyn* in Wales, is the narrow, serrated ridge which is produced by the close juxtaposition of two glaciated slopes. The most striking *cribau* occur where two cirques are positioned back to back so that their walls present a sheer drop on either side. These arêtes make fascinating ridge walking, and it is not surprising that the most famous walk of its kind in Britain, the Snowdon Horseshoe, provides a fine example, the most remarkable section of which lies between Crib Goch (107, 626553) and Crib-y-Ddysgl (611552). This section is depicted in Fig. 74. The Horseshoe Walk continues over the summit of Snowdon via Bwlch y

FIG. 74. Crib Goch, the well-known ridge walk, with near-vertical drops on either side. Behind is the summit of Snowdon (*left background*) and to the right the walk runs over Crib-y-Ddysgl (3,493 feet).

Saethau to Lliwedd, and, consisting mostly of arêtes, is an excursion which the inexperienced should avoid in frost, snow, high wind or cloud. A further equally spectacular (if less famous) example lies immediately to the west of the main Snowdon range, where a serrated ridge runs from Y Garn (5552) over Mynydd Drws-y-Coed and Trum-y-Ddysgl to Mynydd Tal-y-Mignedd (5351).

Other examples are Craig y Fan-ddu (141, 0518) and Rhiw yr Ysgyfarnog (0119), both on the Brecon Beacons, the striking mountain of Cnicht (116 or 107, 6446) which is often mistaken for Snowdon viewed from the Portmadoc embankment ('The Cobb', p. 117), the north-east ridge of Moel Siabod (7155), the south-east ridge of Aran Fawddwy at Drws Bach (116, 8621), and Y Gribyn (107, 6558), a taxing northward spur of the Glyder Range north-east of Snowdon.

The 'horn' feature which results from back-to-back glacial excavation in four directions, and which is so common in the Alps, has nowhere been perfectly developed in Wales. Moelwyn Mawr (107, or 116, 655448) is the nearest approach, and Cnicht has been called 'the Welsh Matterhorn', but it hardly deserves this title.

GLACIATED PLATEAUX

The contrasts between the effects of valley glaciation and sheet glaciation have already been emphasised, and the major characteristic landforms resulting from erosion by valley glaciers have been studied. We now turn to the effects of ice-sheets. The most extensive of these to affect Wales was, of course, the Irish Sea ice-sheet, but this is notable more for its depositional and indirect effects (all of which are dealt with later) than for its erosional features. To illustrate the effects of sheet *erosion* by ice, it is necessary to consider the stretches of plateau in certain locations in the Welsh mountains, whose relief was not sufficiently rugged and varied for valley glaciers to develop, but which developed small ice-caps that succeeded, over a relatively small area, in burying the whole landscape. These areas, as has been noted, represent on a much smaller scale the landforms characteristic of such areas as the Canadian and Baltic Shields which were submerged by continental ice-sheets during the Ice Age.

Much of the interior of Wales consists of large areas of plateau at various heights. During the Ice Age, the former gently undulating surface was stripped of any soil cover and transformed into a disarray

FIG. 75. Undulating, rocky topography characteristic of a glaciated plateau. The lake is Llyn Teifi in interior Cardiganshire.

of rock-knobs, marshy depressions, irregular lakes and indeterminate drainage. *Roches moutonnées* (see below) protrude through a thin veneer of drift and there is a dire lack of easily recognisable landmarks, making this the most dangerous type of landscape in Wales for the walker in misty weather. Most characteristic of all are the lakes. The example illustrated (Fig. 75) is Llyn Teifi (127, 7967), at the source of the Teifi at 1,369 feet in the interior of Cardiganshire; it is of typical irregular, angular shape, set amidst an undulating, soil-stripped countryside of rocky hillocks and bogs. Few such lakes reach any notable depth; Llyn Morynion (116, 7342), on the Migneint Plateau of northern Merioneth, has a maximum depth of only 44 feet, but many other plateau lakes are probably shallower. Some of these lakes, in areas where the incoming streams are loaded with drift-derived sediment, are rapidly filling, indeed some have done so already to leave extensive areas of treacherous marsh; others have little inflow or catchment area, so that the main agent of destruction is the action of the lake itself in eroding its own banks during periods of stormy weather.

Many of these glaciated plateaux in Wales are of but limited extent; however, they are amongst the most distinctive and characteristic of Welsh landscapes. Some examples are the Migneint Plateau already referred to, the area north-west of Betws-y-Coed around Llyn Bodgynnydd (107, 7659), and the south-western section of the Denbigh Moors north of Cerrigydrudion (108, 4895). The interior of Cardiganshire contains many such areas; besides the one illustrated there is the area between Glaslyn (127, 8294) and Bugeilyn (8292) farther north, and the stretch between Llyn Crugnant (140, 7561), Llyn Berwyn (7457) and Llyn Du (7761) farther south.

It is worth noting that the plateau areas farther east, such as the Radnor Forest and Mynydd Epynt, have not been glaciated to this marked degree; here the snowfall was lighter due to their more westerly locations, and the lakes and *roches moutonnées* which punctuate the more westerly plateaux are absent. The drainage is less haphazard and there are fewer areas of marshland.

ROCHES MOUTONNÉES

Roches moutonnées represent in one landform the two basic erosive mechanisms of ice, namely smoothing and plucking. The

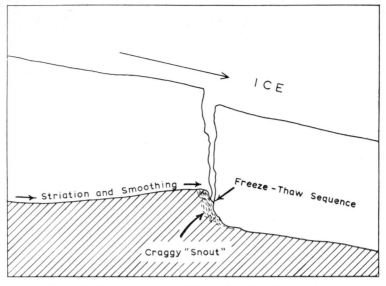

ICE

→ Striation and Smoothing →

Freeze-Thaw Sequence

Craggy "Snout"

FIG. 76. Suggested mode of formation of *roche moutonnée*.

form shows the direction of ice movement in that the 'upstream' side is smoothed and striated by the advance of the glacier, armed with rock debris in its sole. So much is clear, but the cause of the craggy profile on the 'downstream' side is not so obvious. It is undoubtedly due in many cases to actual plucking by the glacier of sections of well-jointed rock, but in others a process akin to 'basal sapping' as described by W. D. Johnson (p. 85) may be responsible (Fig. 76).

The single example illustrated (Fig. 77) is an almost perfect one. Aligned from north to south in the Vale of Ffestiniog, it is a landmark for miles around and plainly shows the direction of ice movement from right (north) to left (south), with its long smooth slope on the north side and bare rock exposed. The craggy snout overlooking the farm on the extreme left faces down the Vale, and probably marks the location of an icefall or series of crevasses during the glacial era. The feature, together with another equally obvious example behind it, dominates the western or left-hand side of the Dolgellau/Blaenau–Ffestiniog main road as it enters the built-up area of the latter south of Congl-y-wal (116 or 107, 7044).

The plural form of the French name for this feature infers that these rocky hillocks are usually found in considerable numbers together. Welsh examples, however, rarely conform to this, neither do they seem likely to be mistaken for sheep from any distance. The name itself, therefore, is inappropriate in Wales, since the best examples usually occur singly or in groups of two or three. They occur very frequently in the glaciated valleys of North Wales, particularly in the Lledr valley near Dolwyddelan (107, 7352), and in the Ogwen valley upstream of Bethesda. Unfortunately, the feature does not emerge well on a map of scale 1 inch to a mile, and only rarely on maps of scale 2½ inches to the mile. Readers should be able to recognise any local examples, however, having seen the general form which they take. The most common locations are in the bottoms of the wider glaciated valleys and distributed across the glaciated plateaux referred to earlier. Like ribbon lakes, they are much more common in the mountains of the north-western counties than elsewhere.

MARGINAL LAKES AND OVERFLOW CHANNELS

Temporary accumulations of water during the Ice Age were caused by the obstruction of the normal drainage by the ice-front. The most extensive of these marginal lakes in Wales were probably at their height during the retreat of the glaciers, when vast quantities

FIG. 77. *Roche moutonnée* near Blaenau Ffestiniog, Merioneth.

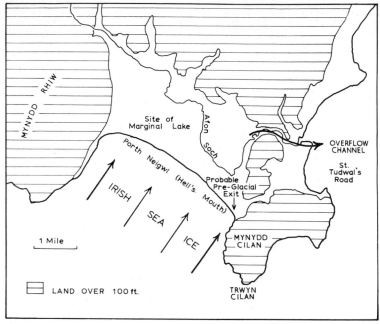

FIG. 78. Glacial diversion of Afon Soch, Llŷn, Caernarvonshire.

of meltwater added their volume to the already obstructed drainage. These marginal lakes never lasted long enough to produce fertile lacustrine plains as in the Red River Plains of North Dakota and southern Manitoba, and the most striking Welsh landforms for which they are responsible are the remarkable *overflow channels* or *spillways* which were cut by the final drainage as it overflowed at successive lowest points on the rim of the marginal lake. In certain cases, the supply of overflow water was sufficiently copious and protracted to enable the issuing stream to cut down the level of the outlet to the extent that the marginal lake was completely drained, and the post-glacial drainage was diverted along the spillway so formed, as happened in the case of the Ironbridge gorge on the Severn in England. In other instances in Wales the overflow lasted long enough to cut a channel through the rim of the marginal lake, only for the original drainage to be resumed after the retreat of the impeding glacier.

Examples of both types are, however, to be found. Of the first category is the gorge of Afon Soch, west of Abersoch in the

Llŷn Peninsula. The pre-glacial exit of the Soch was into Porth Neigwl to the south-west (Fig. 78), but this exit was blocked by the retreating Irish Sea ice, which added meltwater to the impeded drainage. The result was that a marginal lake was impounded which overflowed eastwards into St. Tudwal's Road. This overflow was maintained over a long enough period for the outlet to be cut down almost to (or, possibly, below) the present sea-level, and after the withdrawal of the ice from Hell's Mouth, Afon Soch now continued to use the overflow gorge rather than the more direct exit into Hell's Mouth.

Similarly, the Dee at Berwyn (Fig. 50) has been diverted through an overflow channel (108 or 117, 200433) cut across the neck of the incised meander to the north during a late stage of the glacial period when meltwater was abundant and the former course of the river in the loop to the north was plugged by stagnant ice (Wills, 1912).

A further minor example occurs in north-east Monmouthshire, where the ice moving south-eastwards off the Black Mountains and down the Usk valley impounded a small lake in the upper Troddi basin around Llanvapley (142, 3614) and Llantilio Crossenny (3914). This overflowed eastwards down the present course of the Troddi into the Wye via a spillway which again became sufficiently entrenched to retain the post-glacial drainage.

A spectacular and well-known dry valley is the Mochdre valley (107, 8278) which carries the main road A55 and the main Holyhead–London railway between Llandudno Junction and Colwyn Bay. Embleton (1961) suggests that glacial interference is the most acceptable explanation for this relief feature. During the pre-glacial period, the Conway entered Penrhyn Bay near Colwyn Bay via the Mochdre valley, with a low ridge of Ordovician volcanic rocks joining Conway Mountain (7677) to Deganwy Hill (354 feet, 7879). In a subsequent phase of deglaciation, the Mochdre valley was blocked at its northern end by a shrinking lobe of Irish Sea ice (p. 75). Meltwaters from this ice and also from the Conway glacier then breached the Conway–Deganwy ridge, thus providing the post-glacial course of the Conway.

Rather more common in Wales, however, are examples of the second category, where conspicuous channels have been cut which were too high to retain the drainage after the return of normal conditions. In southern Cardiganshire and northern Pembrokeshire, the Irish Sea ice impeded the drainage of the lower Teifi, Nevern

H

and other smaller streams, so that a succession of marginal lakes
was impounded. These lakes overspilled southwards into each other,
the final exit being down the Gwaun valley into the Bristol Channel.
Connecting the lower valleys of these rivers, therefore, is a series of
overflow channels, some of the largest being Nant-y-Bugail (151,
9832), Esgyrn Bottom (9734) and the valley of the Crinei Brook
(9634). All these show the characteristic flat floor and steep side of
overflow channels, and none of them could have been cut by the
tiny streams occupying them now. The Dinas valley (Fig. 79)
behind Dinas Head (138, 0040) is a perfect example of this form,
since it contains no permanent stream at all. Its floor is flat and
ill-drained; its clean-cut sides steep and well-wooded.

Farther east near Swansea are found the Dunvant and Brynhyfryd
channels. The most obvious explanation of the formation of these
is that the Irish Sea ice impeded the southward drainage of the
River Loughor together with its tributaries Llan and Lliw, thus
impounding a large marginal lake in the lower sections of these
valleys (Fig. 80). It would thus be assumed that this lake overflowed
initially eastwards via the Brynhyfryd gap, which runs from the
vicinity of Cockett Station (153, 632950) through Cwmbwrla into
the lower Tawe valley. A second minor channel running across

FIG. 79. Overflow channel: Dinas valley, Pembrokeshire. During Pleistocene times the Irish Sea ice-sheet, coming in from Cardigan Bay (*left*),
blocked west-flowing drainage into Newport Bay (*background*). Great
quantities of meltwater then overflowed southwards *via* this channel.

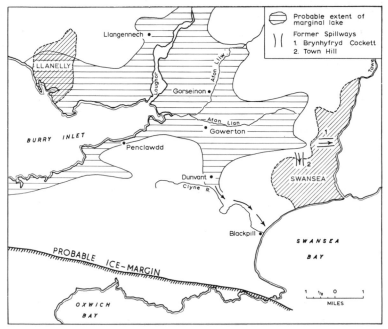

FIG. 80. Suggested formation of Dunvant overflow channel,
near Swansea, Glamorgan.

Townhill southwards through the present site of Sketty was thus
abandoned before the Brynhyfryd gap, since its level is about
100 feet higher.

With the further recession of the Irish Sea ice, the level of this
marginal lake would fall, causing in turn the abandonment of the
Brynhyfryd channel. During the later stages of the retreat, when the
ice-front lay presumably across Mumbles Head and Cefn Bryn
(Gower), the overflow was finding its way out into the ice-free
Swansea Bay via what is now the most striking of all three spillways,
that running south through the present location of Dunvant. This
deep cleft shows evidence of its origin in its flat bottom and steep
sides, and is drained only by two small brooks which are plainly
'misfits'. By this route the meltwater emerged southwards into the
Clyne valley and finally out into Swansea Bay.

The absence of strand-lines and other evidence of old lake shores
in the Loughor, Llan and Lliw valleys makes it difficult to be
dogmatic concerning this explanation of the formation of the
channels. It is, however, virtually certain that they are meltwater

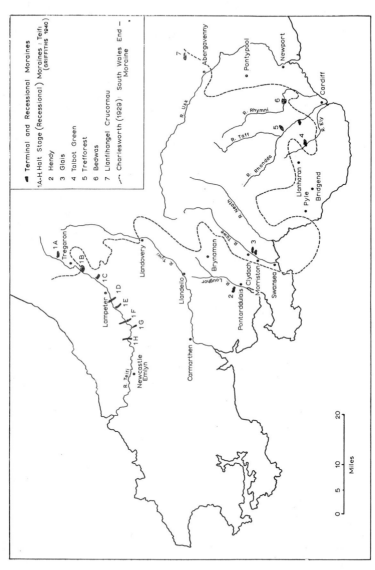

FIG. 81. Terminal and recessional moraines in South Wales.

channels of some kind. None of them was able to retain the main drainage after the final withdrawal of the ice, and all three, together with those of the Teifi–Nevern system, represent the second, or abandoned type of spillway.

MORAINES

Examples of glacial deposition have not attained the widespread recognition accorded to landforms such as Llyn Cau and Nant Ffrancon in the field of glacial erosion. However, several excellent examples of moraines exist, most Welsh valley glaciers having produced terminal or recessional moraines where the glacier remained stationary for a while as the rate of melting exactly matched the rate of advance.

The most striking development of these moraines is found in South Wales, where Charlesworth (1929) attempted to trace the course of the moraines which accumulated at the edges of the valley glaciers of the local Welsh ice in the last glaciation. Prominent transverse moraines are found in the valleys of the Teifi, Tywi, Loughor, Tawe, Neath, Ely, Taff and Rhymni (Fig. 81). In the Teifi, eight successive moraines represent halt-stages in the retreat of the Teifi glacier, the most northerly being at Tregaron (140, 6759);

FIG. 82. Morainic dam across the Tawe valley between Glais and Clydach, 6 miles north of Swansea, Glamorgan.

in the Loughor valley a moraine may be detected between Pontar-
ddulais and Hendy by study of the 1-inch O.S. map (153, 5905 and
5904). Further conspicuous transverse moraines are found at Glais
in the Tawe valley (see below), and also at Aberdulais in the Neath
valley (153, 7699), west of Talbot Green in the Ely valley (154, 0383,
note the 200-foot contour west of the bus station), east of Bedwas
in the Rhymni valley (154, 1788), and north of Abergavenny at
Llanfihangel Crucornau (142, 3120, note the cutting through the
moraine north of the station).

The Glais moraine (Fig. 82) is a mile-long dam of boulder clay
about 5 miles up the Tawe valley from Swansea. Two other
moraines can clearly be detected between Glais and Swansea
(153, 6897 and 6695); these are all part of a complex of glacial
deposition in and around the lower Tawe valley which Charlesworth
regarded as part of his South Wales end-moraine. Strahan (1907)
recognised that the general shape of the Glais moraine corresponded
closely with the form of contemporary ice-front accumulations then
being studied. The northern slope, produced by the advance and
retreat of the ice-front over the debris, is gentle, though broken by
transverse ridges, but the southern slope is as steep as the material
will stand. Washed out from the snout is an extensive 'apron' of
outwash gravels, which can be traced on the 1-inch map in the path
of the 50-foot contour south of the moraine as far as Felin Fran.
The maximum height attained by the dam is about 140 feet above
the valley floor; there may have been an accumulation of water
behind it, but there is no conclusive evidence to support this.

At Tregaron, however, the moraine is very broad, and clearly
succeeded in damming a very large lake in which considerable
thicknesses of a stiff, blue-grey lacustrine clay were deposited,
probably during the period before the surrounding countryside had
regained its plant-cover, and thus the incoming streams were highly
charged with sediment, (Godwin and Mitchell, 1938). The Teifi finally
cut a niche in the morainic dam and the lake drained, its former
extent now being marked by Cors Goch Glan Teifi, where a thickness of some feet of peat has developed on top of the lacustrine clay.

The moraines of North Wales, although equally widespread, are
generally less striking than those of South Wales. They are found
at the mouth of almost every side valley where it enters the main
valley, and on the lips of cirques. They have contributed to the
level of certain lakes also, notably Llyn Idwal, where there are four

successive recessional moraines on the lip (p. 83). Mention must also be made of the crescent-shaped moraine of Cwm Graianog, clearly visible from the main trunk road A5 across the valley a mile or so south of Bethesda; a small, but perfect example.

Lateral moraines, carried along on the surface of the ice, are caused by the accumulation of falling rock on either edge of the glacier, and most Welsh glaciated *cymoedd* show debris of this origin. A merger of two such moraines at the confluence of two glaciers produces the accumulation known as a medial moraine. An interesting example of this is found in the Rhymni valley, where a tapering moraine accumulated between the Rhymni and Darran glaciers (154, 149005) at Bargoed.

ERRATICS

An erratic is a boulder or rock composed of material which it is known did not originate where it is found. To deduce the directions and extent of the ice-flows which affected any area is a process of interpreting circumstantial evidence. The geologist has to follow up clues in much the same way as a detective, erratics being to the former what fingerprints are to the latter. By investigating the nature, and thus determining the origin of boulders and pebbles found in glacial deposits, the geologist collects valuable evidence to support that obtained from striations on rocks and onset-and-lee features, and with it he builds up a picture of the origin of the ice, the route taken, and, above all, the maximum extent of ice from a particular source.

In North Wales, erratics form the principal evidence from which the relative extents of ice from the two source regions (the Irish Sea and the mountains) are deduced. In Anglesey, boulders tend to be strewn in a south-westerly direction from their source region; witness the spread of hornblende picrite south-west across the island through Llanerchymedd (Figs. 83 and 84), and the Garth Ferry grits along the shore of the Menai Straits, from their source opposite Bangor south-west past Menai Bridge. Lake District rocks such as Eskdale granite frequently occur in the Anglesey and Llŷn drift, as also on the Cheshire Plain, thus confirming the division of the Irish Sea ice into the two 'arms' previously referred to. The maximum extent of the Irish Sea ice in North Wales can be demonstrated by the occurrence of patches of sand containing marine

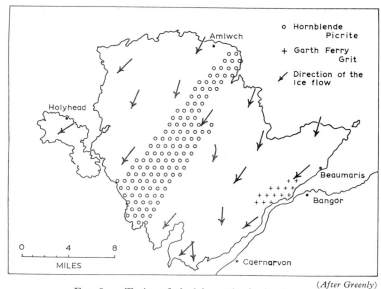

Amlwch

o   Hornblende
        Picrite
+   Garth Ferry
        Grit
⟋   Direction of the
      ice flow

Holyhead

Beaumaris

Bangor

0   4   8
MILES

Caernarvon

(After Greenly)

FIG. 83.   Trains of glacial erratics in Anglesey.

FIG. 84.   Erratic boulder of hornblende picrite, Mynydd Mwyn Mawr, Anglesey.   This boulder has been brought south-westwards from its source region by the Irish Sea ice-sheet.

shells on the northern slopes of the mountains of the mainland. On Moel Tryfan, 5 miles south-east of Caernarvon, these patches occur at heights of nearly 1,400 feet above sea-level. By these means, a composite picture can be built up of the penetration of the Irish Sea ice into North Wales (Fig. 85).

A study of erratics in the Middle Welsh borderland shows that the powerful glaciers which moved east off Plynlimon and the associated hills of west Central Wales over-rode all but the most

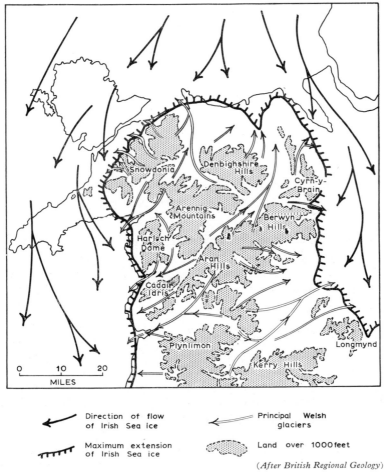

Direction of flow of Irish Sea ice		Principal Welsh glaciers	
Maximum extension of Irish Sea ice		Land over 1000 feet	

(After British Regional Geology)

FIG. 85.   Penetration of Irish Sea ice into North Wales.

important hill-groups. The Radnor Forest, where erratics from Central Wales are found at heights of 1,750 feet O.D., does not appear to have been a centre of ice-dispersal, but the Black Mountains can safely be said to have carried an ice-cap, for drift in the valleys is entirely of local origin, and there are no erratics at all to be found from more westerly areas.

In South Wales, the distribution of the moraines associated with the southward limit of the local Welsh ice has already been noted. The Irish Sea ice, however, came in across the region from Cardigan Bay. It was powerful enough to over-ride the Prescelly Mountains, and invaded south Pembrokeshire and Carmarthenshire, Gower and the Vale of Glamorgan from the west. Evidence for this is once again supplied by erratics derived from distant shores of the Irish Sea, which have been discovered in all these areas; they include pebbles of Ailsa Craig and Goat Fell granite from western Scotland and others which can be matched in the Southern Uplands. The actual direction taken by this ice (Fig. 86) is well demonstrated by the frequent occurrences in south Carmarthenshire and Gower of erratics from Pembrokeshire sources, particularly of quartz-feldspar from Ramsey Island. Felsite pebbles from North Wales have been collected near Cardiff; this is the most easterly extent of the erratics associated with the Irish Sea ice in South Wales.

DRUMLINS

The origin of these egg-shaped hills is the least clear of all the glaciated landforms dealt with hitherto. The essential characteristics are an oval shape, and a steep slope facing the direction of ice advance, with a gentle tapering both altitudinally and laterally in the direction of ice retreat. Wide variations, however, are common. Drumlins can rarely be recognised singly, although similarly shaped mounds of typical drumlin height (60–100 feet) do frequently occur in Wales, as, for instance, in the wind-gap west of Cerrigydrudion (p. 59). If, however, it is accepted that true drumlins must occur in numbers together, then there are only three areas in Wales which can be regarded as possessing conspicuous drumlinoid features. These are the Caerphilly Basin, where they are prominent to the north and east of the town alongside the roads up and down the Rhymni valley, the Hirwaun/Rhigos region of North Glamorganshire and the Anglesey/Llŷn platforms.

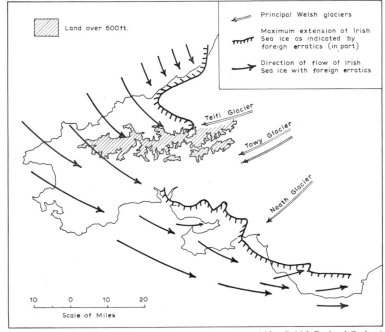

(After British Regional Geology)

FIG. 86.   Penetration of Irish Sea ice into South Wales.

It is thought that drumlins correspond to patches in the sole of the ice overloaded with debris, which slowed down the movement of the ice sections so charged, thereby causing deposition.   The streamlined form of the drumlin is taken to mean that the clear ice moulded the depositions beneath the over-charged patches into this form and aligned them in the direction of ice-flow.   Also, the classic British examples (the Eden valley between the Lake District and the Pennines, and around Lough Neagh in Northern Ireland) seem to show a marked correspondence to areas of ice congestion.   How far do the Welsh drumlins agree with these generalisations?

Little work has been done on Welsh drumlins as such; the best studied examples are those of the region between and around Hirwaun and Rhigos (154, 9505 and 9106), between the Neath and Cynon valleys in northern Glamorgan (Griffiths, 1940).   Their alignment is not always apparent, but those near the Cynon, broadly speaking, trend south-east–north-west, and those near the Neath north-east–south-west; between these districts, the alignment is

approximately north–south. Undoubtedly this was a region of great
ice-congestion, having accumulated ice off the Brecon Beacons to
the north as well as from the higher stretches of the South Wales
Coalfield Plateau to the south, so that the drumlins formed there
support the somewhat obscure explanation of their origin which is
given above. Good examples can be seen on both sides of the road
to Brecon A4059 north of the railway bridge at 952062, between
Hirwaun and the near-by industrial estate, and alongside A4061 for
the last half-mile before its junction with A465. In the last instance,
the main road has actually been cut through a drumlin in at least
one place.

The Anglesey drumlins, on the other hand, do not appear to
correspond with any area of ice-congestion. This must have been
greatest in the south-east nearest the mainland, where the Snowdonia
ice-cap was diverting the Irish Sea ice-sheet to the south-west. The
best examples of drumlin-topography, however, are found in the
north-west, where the drainage is typically indeterminate, around
Bodedern (105, 3380), Bryngwran (3577), Llanfachreth (3182) and
Valley (2979). Several lakes have been impounded amidst the
irregular mounds of boulder clay, and the trend of many of these
mounds is markedly south-westward, as, indeed, is that of the lakes.

FIG. 87.   Drumlin country near Valley, Anglesey.

This alignment, however, is by no means universal, and the example depicted, which is on the north-east side of the trunk road A5 about a mile south-east of Valley, actually presents a steep front to the south-east (Fig. 87).

There is no reason to suppose that the ice in this region was in any marked degree overcharged, and these drumlins of north-west Anglesey may well be the remains of a mantle of boulder clay which has been etched into drumlinoid form by meltwater from the ice-sheet. Certainly, many of the intervening dells show typical signs of having been eroded by copious water flows, and although this hypothesis has been rejected in general principle, it would appear to fit the facts more closely in this particular instance.

COASTAL FEATURES

It has already been noted how, in the case of the work of streams, landscape evolution follows a definite cycle, governed basically by base-level. The application of this principle to the work of ice is not rewarding, as the control of gravity over the erosive power of glaciers is not so rigid as in the case of rivers. While it is tempting to envisage a cycle of ice crosion based upon a temperature 'base-level' (where rejuvenation is produced by a renewed onset of frigid conditions), the study of individual landforms cannot be directly related to the cycle as can the evolution of a stream-moulded landscape. The work of wind does not appear to be in any substantial degree cyclic in nature.

The study of coastal features does, however, repay an approach based on the cyclic principle, and there is a marked analogy with the work of streams. There appears to be in both cases a pronounced sequence of events which eventually produces a stagnant stage that can only be interrupted by a change in base-level. However, in the case of coastal features, either an uplift of the land (*i.e.* a coastal *emergence*) or a subsidence (*submergence*) can rejuvenate the cycle. Positive and negative *eustatic* movements of sea-level can also produce submergence and emergence respectively. Coastlines where the dominant features are the results of submergence are known as *coastlines of submergence*, while *coastlines of emergence* are produced where the dominant features result from the gain of land upon the sea,

This apparently clear-cut division is, in fact, often difficult to interpret, and nowhere is this more applicable than in Wales. A superficial examination of the coastline would support an initial diagnosis of submergence, the sinewy inlet of Milford Haven and the indented character of the Cardigan Bay coast are obviously the results of the post-glacial drowning of the lower parts of former river valleys. The relation between this submergence and tales of Welsh folk-lore concerning 'Cantre'r Gwaelod' (which was said to have disappeared under Cardigan Bay due to the carelessness of a watchman) has been discussed by Steers (1948) and North (1957). They conclude that the 'folk tales' which tell the story of the disaster in some detail are a product of comparatively modern times, and are to be discounted in this form. Nevertheless, it is almost certain that substantial subsidence took place in Cardigan Bay before the advent of the Bronze Age, *i.e.* probably in Neolithic times, and the possibility that the tales contain a germ of truth handed down over this far longer time-span must be acknowledged.

However, the Tertiary Period in Wales saw a series of emergent adjustments in base level, which Brown and others take to have produced a series of uplifted peneplains in the interior (p. 32). Moreover, around the coast of Wales is found a series of platforms at heights varying from between 200 and 700 feet above sea-level, which have probably been formed by wave planation followed by emergence of the resulting platform (p. 118). While, therefore, submergence is the principal element brought out in the shape of the *coastline*, a relatively minor submergence is only the most recent of a considerable series of movements with respect to sea-level, the dominant character of which has, in fact, been emergent.

The main difficulty of interpretation lies in the fact that while features of submergence invariably occur *at the coast*, emergence (although it may sometimes react upon the actual coastline) often produces important features which are now situated well inland. It is thus questionable whether such landforms (*e.g.* marine platforms) can be regarded as coastal features. From the point of view of location, they obviously cannot be so classed, but since the classification embodies a genetic (*i.e.* causal) approach, then it is justifiable to include them as coastal features, since their initial planation took place at the shoreline. They are thus treated under 'Emergent Features'.

It is not proposed to derive a purely academic generalisation as to whether any particular section of the Welsh coast is predominantly

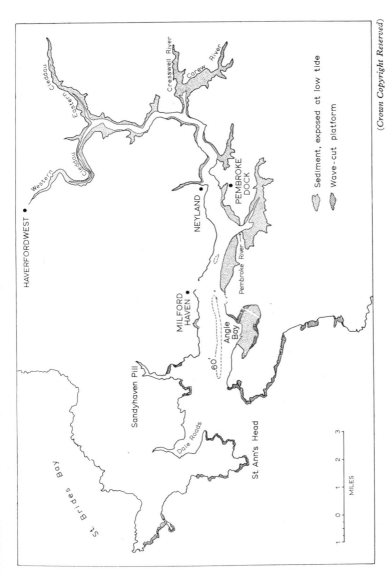

Fig. 88. The drowned valley system of Milford Haven, Pembrokeshire.

emergent or submergent in character. What is important is to locate and interpret the major individual coastal features, and to recognise their place in the respective cycles of erosion, submergent or emergent.

FEATURES DUE TO SUBMERGENCE

The inundation of any area of land by the sea is hardly likely to result in a smooth coastline. The lower reaches of the valleys and tributaries leading into the coast will be flooded, and the coastline will follow the former contour pattern, producing a shoreline punctured with sinewy indentations of a shape broadly determined by the pre-submergent pattern of river drainage.

These indentations are, in Wales, all of the *ria* form, *i.e.* they are drowned river valleys. In western Scotland most of the valleys were severely glaciated even down to the coast level, and this has resulted in the deep, steep-sided, fiord-like inlets called sea-lochs. The most profound effects of highland glaciation in Wales, on the other hand, are found near the cores of the glaciated uplands, which no post-glacial advance of the sea has been able to reach. The inlets of the coastline of Wales do not, in consequence, show any marked glacial over-deepening below sea-level, although the rock-floor of the lower Tawe is, in places, over 150 feet below the present sea-level, due mostly to post-glacial subsidence and infilling.

The initial stage in submergence is very well illustrated by Milford Haven (Figs. 88 and 89). This ria represents an early form in a coastline of submergence, and is really the young stage of one of the cycles of marine denudation. The submergence of both the main valley and its tributaries is clearly demonstrated, but it can be seen how the calm water of the Haven has encouraged the deposition of sediment by the streams flowing into it, especially in the Pembroke, Carew, Cresswell, East and West Cleddau and Sandy Haven Pill estuaries, where there are already considerable expanses of flats exposed at low tide. It is significant that these accumulations have, in every case, failed so far to encroach upon the deepest part of the Haven, where the water is more turbulent.

The second stage begins with wave-attack on the exposed headlands seaward of the drowned valley. *Wave-cut platforms* (p. 125) will be etched into the headlands, with some of the material removed being deposited to seaward as a *wave-built platform* (Fig. 90). The rest of the material thus eroded from the headlands is

FIG. 89. Milford Haven, Pembrokeshire. This complex system of water-ways was formed by the submergence of a system of river valleys. Since this photograph was taken the Esso Oil Refinery has been constructed on the north (*right*) shore at Herbrandston, a little to the left and seaward of the cloud ; slightly farther up the inlet on the opposite shore stands the B.P. oil terminal at Popton Point.

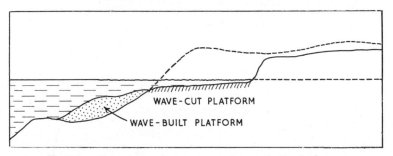

WAVE-CUT PLATFORM

WAVE-BUILT PLATFORM

FIG. 90.   Formation of wave-cut and wave-built platforms.

deposited either in the relatively calm water of the head of a bay (thus giving a *bay-head beach*), or as *spits* across the mouths of inlets. Spits tend to form where the shoreline is sharply indented and where there is a pronounced drift of material along the shore (Fig. 91).

I

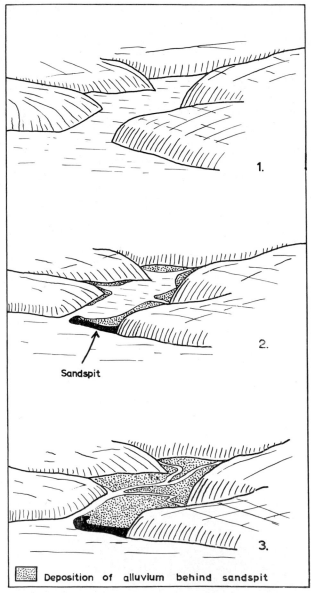

1.

2.

Sandspit

3.

Deposition of alluvium behind sandspit

FIG. 91.   Stages in the silting-up of a submerged river valley

Bay-head beaches, however, form where the indentations in the coastline are more open and less angular.   In either case, however, the tendency is clear; the coastline is being made smoother, and deposition is playing an increasingly important part.   The shoreline

FIG. 92.   Whitmore Bay, Barry Island, Glamorgan.   Man, capitalising upon the natural endowment of a gently-sloping bay-head beach of fine sand, has added a comprehensive amusement park, together with the other activities sought by holiday-makers.

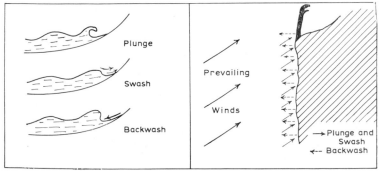

FIG. 93.   The development of longshore drift.

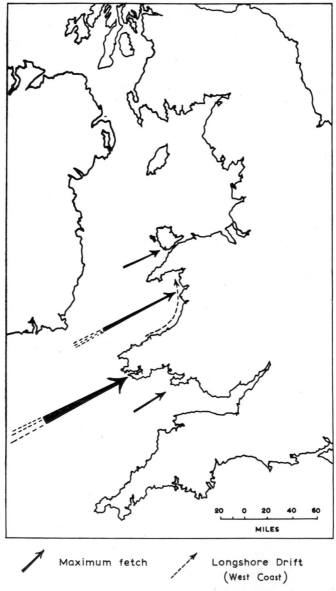

Maximum fetch   Longshore Drift
                                  (West Coast)

FIG. 94.   Direction of longshore drift on the west coast of Wales.

now becomes much less angular, loses its youth and adopts a more mature outline. In this way we can recognise the progress of a distinct cycle of marine denudation and its effect upon the shape of the coastline. Fine instances of bay-head beaches occur at Barry Island (Fig. 92), Coney Beach, Porthcawl (153, 8276) along the Gower coast at Langland Bay (153, 6087) and Caswell Bay (5987), in Pembrokeshire at Marloes Sands (151, 7807), at Cricieth in South Caernarvonshire (116, 5037), at Llandudno and Colwyn Bay (Sheet 107) on the north coast, and at Cemaes (106, 3793) and Traeth Bychan (5184) in Anglesey.

The Cardigan Bay coast in north Cardigan and Merioneth

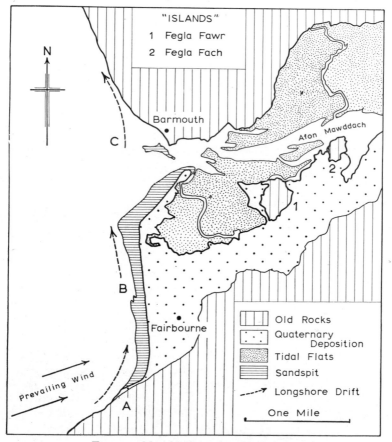

FIG. 95. Mawddach estuary, Merioneth.

FIG. 96. A sandspit barring the Mawddach estuary, Fairbourne, Merioneth. Debris eroded from the cliffs of Gallt Ffynnon-yr-Hydd (*background*) has been brought northwards by the longshore drift to form the spit along which runs the Fairbourne Miniature Railway, much used by summer visitors.

presents three superb instances of maturity in the cycle, namely the estuaries of the Dovey, Mawddach and Dwyryd. Each must originally have been a broad ria formed by the subsidence of an original river valley and some degree of glacial modification, although it is unlikely that extensive over-deepening took place. In the original ria there were a few islands, still referred to locally by the name 'Ynys'.

The attack of the waves upon the exposed headlands on either side of these rias released enormous quantities of eroded material, which was moved along the shore by *longshore drift* (Figs. 93 and 94). An additional factor has been the presence of considerable deposits of boulder clay banked up against the cliffs of the west coast. These deposits have supplied great quantities of pebbles and boulders which have been washed northwards along the shore. In the case of the Mawddach estuary (Fig. 95), the debris at the foot of Gallt-Ffynnon-yr-Hydd (A) was moved forward obliquely with the prevailing onshore wind as the waves broke, and then down the beach with the backwash, usually approximately at right angles to the shoreline, in a direction determined by the beach-slope and not by the prevailing wind. This continuous *swash* and *backwash* produced a resultant motion of the debris along the beach in the direction indicated, finally depositing the pebbles and other finer material in the calmer water across the ria mouth, and building across a spit (B) from the south shore of the ria. The continuing vitality of the longshore drift is well illustrated at Barmouth (C), where the groynes which traverse the beach have already been almost covered by the piling up of debris against their southern edges.

Behind this spit (Fig. 96), the calm water became ideal for the deposition of sediment brought down by the rivers tributary to the ria. Considerable areas have thus been built up to about sea-level, and, while liable to occasional floods, these can be regarded as dry land. Where embankments have been constructed, the land may prove to be useful agriculturally, although the peaty soil is extremely acid and unproductive. Much of what is not dry land is, in fact, exposed at low tide, and here deposition actively continues where the water is tidal without being affected by wave action to any marked degree. Eventually, the whole of the former ria will be built up in this way, with a meandering river Mawddach the only remaining important channel in its floor.

By a similar process Borth Bog, or Cors Fochno (127, 6089) in north Cardiganshire has been built up behind the spit at Borth, and farther north, a complex ria system is being gradually filled up in the Dwyryd and Glaslyn estuaries. A three-mile, dune-covered spit running north from Harlech has sealed off both estuaries, that of the Dwyryd being known as the Traeth Bach, and the dry land immediately behind the Harlech spit as Morfa Harlech. The extensive stretch of water (Traeth Mawr) which formerly existed behind Portmadoc and which washed the margins of Garreg (107 or 116, 6141) and Prenteg (5841) was dramatically reclaimed in 1811 by W. A. Madocks through the construction of an embankment known as The Cobb.

Ill-drained coastal flats usually go by the name 'Morfa' in Wales. 'Cors' is a more general term, which is applied to marshy or boggy stretches of territory. Neither term, however, can be strictly identified with any specific class of coastal feature.

That Milford Haven has not yet advanced beyond the young stage is due to the fact that its mouth directly faces the prevailing winds and there is consequently no pronounced longshore drift. Moreover, the water at its mouth is more turbulent than that of the former Dovey, Mawddach and Dwyryd rias, since the mouth faces a long 'fetch' by the prevailing winds across the Atlantic. For all these reasons, spit development is unlikely, although deposition of sediment has already commenced in the sheltered estuaries of the inflowing rivers (Fig. 88), and bay-head beaches have resulted in Angle Bay and Dale Roads owing to the accumulation of debris released by wave attack on the exposed headlands near the mouth of the Haven.

FEATURES DUE TO EMERGENCE

It might appear that the work of the sea, confined as it is to the actual coastline, would be extremely restricted in its effect upon landforms. This is certainly not true of Wales. Emergence of the land due to the many adjustments of Tertiary times has carried features originally a result of coastal action well inland, and the work of the sea is thus in evidence in places 20 miles or more from the present coastline.

The coastal 'plains' of Wales (Fig. 2), in Anglesey, Llŷn, Cardiganshire, south Pembrokeshire and Carmarthenshire, Gower and the Vale of Glamorgan, are mainly composed of a series of uplifted wave-cut platforms, at heights ranging from 200 to 700 feet above sea-level. These emerged marine platforms are often difficult to distinguish from sub-aerial peneplains, but it is fairly clear in Wales that most of the coastal plateau surfaces show evidence of marine planation. The main distinguishing feature is that if the marine platform is young and has not yet been substantially modified by sub-aerial denudation since emergence, the marine planation has apparently proceeded independently of structure, a platform having been eroded across varying rock outcrops and structural lines in a way uncharacteristic of sub-aerial erosion. In addition, many of these marine platforms, particularly the highest, seem to end landward in a marked break of slope which can be taken to be a degraded line of former cliffs.

E. H. Brown (1957(a), 1960) summing up the work of other authors as well as his own, has constructed a map, a simplified form of which is shown in Fig. 97, in which he traces an old coastline of degraded cliffs at a present height of 650–700 feet O.D., with a

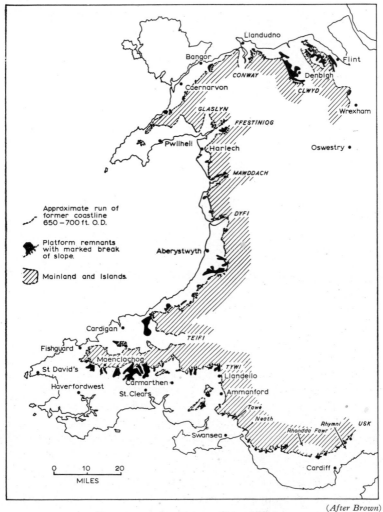

(After Brown)

FIG. 97.   A former coastline of Wales.

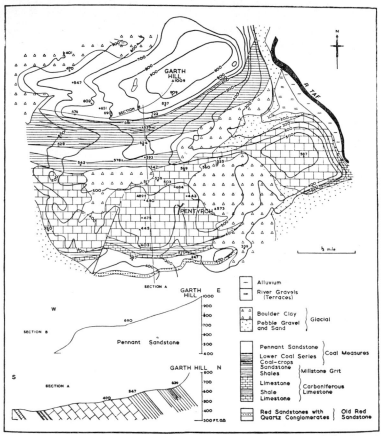

FIG. 98.   Pentyrch platform, Glamorgan.

(After Brown)

marked tendency to the upper limit.   Immediately seaward of this
old coastline is to be found a whole series of uniform summits and
platform remnants at just above 600 feet, which are thought to be
the remains of the wave-cut platform.   Platforms at this level
(*i.e.* just below the old coastline) are most extensively developed in
the south-west, particularly in Pembrokeshire, south Cardiganshire
and south-west Carmarthenshire.   This is consistent with the
direction of maximum 'fetch' of the waves across the Atlantic from
the south-west.   On this coast, facing the prevailing winds un-
sheltered from the open ocean by any land, wave-action would be
most vigorous.   Indeed, it is in this part of Wales that the finest

contemporary examples of wave-cut platforms are to be found.

This old coastline is strikingly parallel with the present one, and it has been reconstructed by plotting those areas where a platform remnant at about 600 feet is backed by a sharp break of slope on the landward side. These remnants are usually highly fractionated, but may easily be detected in certain locations, *e.g.* south and south-east of Maenclochog (139, 0827), Llanycefn (0923) and Llangolman (1126).

The long ridge of Mynydd Prescelly behind Maenclochog is taken to represent part of the old mainland, the steep drop on the south face of which is the degraded cliff-line. The main distinguishing features of a marine platform are illustrated; the platform is cut across a variety of highly folded and faulted rocks, the only dissection of which has been by subsequent stream erosion, and the platform ends landward in a marked break of slope.

Such platforms are very extensive in Pembrokeshire, but elsewhere in South Wales, while often clearly discernible, they are not as extensive as those farther west. In the South Wales Coalfield, they may be found at intervals along the southern rim, particularly north-east of Pentyrch (Fig. 98), near Cardiff (154, 1081), where the south-east face of Garth Hill (1083) drops steeply down on to the old platform (Fig. 99). It is unlikely that this can be an uplifted

FIG. 99.   The Pentyrch platform, viewed from the east.

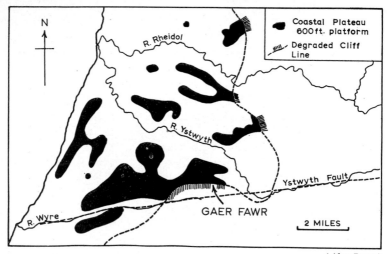

FIG. 100. Ancient embayment of the sea coast south-east of Aberystwyth.

sub-aerial peneplain, for the only adaptations to structure which can be determined are those which have taken place *subsequent* to the formation of the peneplain. For the rest, the surface of the old marine platform is cut across a variety of rock outcrops including Carboniferous Limestone, Millstone Grit and the southern outcrop of the Coal Measures. The most extensive remaining areas are on the Carboniferous Limestone, the weaker shales having been extensively removed by post-emergent erosion.

Farther west in Carmarthenshire, a fine instance of a 600-foot platform backed by a degraded cliff-line lies at the southern end of Mynydd Sylen, an outlier of the Low Peneplain (p. 33) which is taken to have been an 'island' off the now-degraded coastline shown in Fig. 97. The platform is eroded across a gently-dipping outcrop of shales of the Pennant Series supported by an underlying sandstone bed. The degraded cliff itself is cut into the shales and is relatively well preserved.

Amongst the most extensive 600-foot platform remnants in Wales are those south-west of Aberystwyth flanking the lower Ystwyth valley (Fig. 100). The postulated shape of the old coastline here suggests an interesting explanation of the course of the Ystwyth downstream of Llanafan Bridge (127, 6871). The line of degraded cliffs on the north face of Gaer Fawr (6472) and to the north of

Llanafan suggests a former embayment of the sea reaching as far inland as the present Llanafan Bridge. As the sea retreated from this embayment, the Ystwyth extended its course north-westwards, gradually entrenching itself into the platform as it did so. This would explain why the Ystwyth, having established itself along the Ystwyth Fault in its middle section (p. 59), turns to flow away from the fault in its lower stretches. The platform remnants here are extensive, strikingly uniform and are cut across a variety of folded strata.

In North Wales, good examples occur south and south-west of Llandudno where there are several platforms backed by breaks of slope (Sheets 107 and 108). Between the lower Conway and Colwyn Bay is a well-marked series of summits in the range 550–650 feet, which are probably the fractionated remains of a marine platform. The western face of Cefn Du (8373) presents a conspicuous break of slope which is landward of the old platform. These breaks of slope at just under 700 feet may be traced right round the former headland behind Colwyn Bay and become particularly noticeable south-west and south-east of Betws-yn-Rhos (108, 9073). The summit plateau of the Great Orme (107, 7683) is probably an isolated remnant of this same 600-foot platform, the intervening section having been destroyed by both marine and sub-aerial action subsequent to its uplift.

Between this old coastline and the present sea coast there exist a number of other marine platform levels of which two main ones can be recognised, at approximately 200 and 400 feet O.D., with another intermediate one at 330 feet occurring occasionally. The Vale of Glamorgan supplies good illustrations of all these; Cardiff Airport at Rhoose (154, 0667) makes use of the 200-foot platform and the trunk road A48 between Cowbridge and Cardiff travels for much of its course along remnants of the 400-foot platform. A fine view of the former is shown in Fig. 101, the cliffs of over 100 feet at the present coastline and the dissection of the marine platform by subsequent erosion in the foreground being prominent features.

Fig. 106 shows the same 200-foot platform in western Pembrokeshire near St. David's. This striking plain is cut across a variety of sedimentary rocks in the way characteristic of marine planation. The igneous intrusions rising through the platform probably represent ancient sea-stacks and their tops conform either to the 400-foot or 600-foot platforms found farther inland, thus suggesting that they are outliers of the higher marine platforms preserved elsewhere.   In Anglesey, the 'Menaian Platform' recognised by Greenly (1919) represents the 200-foot level, and includes about 400 square miles of country on either side of the Straits.

Around the shores of the Gower Peninsula can be found a series of *raised beaches* of still younger age than these marine platforms. The earliest of these, detectable around the margins of Port Einon (153, 4885) and Oxwich Bay (5286), is known as the *Patella* beach, because of the abundance of limpets it contains.   It is now about 10 feet above high-water mark, and can be correlated with similar features elsewhere in the Bristol and English Channels.   Opening on to this raised beach is a series of caves which were the habitations of prehistoric animals.   These caves were probably excavated, or at least enlarged, by the action of the sea along faults and joints at the same time as the platforms were being planed.   The most famous of these caves are at Paviland (152, 438858) and are known to have been occupied for a considerable time during the latter part of the Old Stone Age.   The Patella beach seems to have been formed during

FIG. 101.   Cliffs flanking Cwm Marcross, Glamorgan.   Note the alternating bands of limestone and relatively soft shale clearly exposed in the cliff face.

an interglacial period, although it had at one time been assumed to be pre-glacial in age.

OTHER COASTAL FEATURES

Since cliffs, sand dunes and storm beaches are coastal landforms which do not conform to the foregoing academic division into emergent and submergent features, they will be treated separately.

Cliffs.—Wales boasts a remarkable variety of cliff scenery which is as much the result of the character of the rocks, their hardness, frequency of joints and faults, reaction to chemical weathering, homogeneity or heterogeneity and stratification, as the severity of wave attack. In Pembrokeshire, where there is probably the most spectacular development of cliffs, differential sea erosion of rocks of varying degrees of hardness is very evident. In the stretch of coast between St. David's Head (138, 721278) and Fishguard, the tough igneous rocks are cut back only very slowly, whereas the softer shales are more rapidly eroded. In consequence, headlands like Strumble Head (Pen Caer 900416) and Trwyn Castell (793316) are composed of igneous rocks, while bays like Traeth Llyfn (802320) and Abereiddi Bay (796312) are carved in shales. On the south side of Llŷn, the eastern extremities of a series of bays eastwards from St. Tudwal's Peninsula (115, 3025) are all marked by small outcrops of resistant igneous rocks which stand out as headlands. One such hard plug (of rhyolite) has steep cliffs on three sides and is crowned by Cricieth Castle (116, 500377).

Soft bands within otherwise hard rocks result in relatively rapid recession of cliffs, fronted by extensive wave-cut platforms. Particularly fine examples of such cliffs and platforms occur in the Lias limestone all along the Vale of Glamorgan coast, that at Marcross (154, 9168, Fig. 101) being typical. The vertical cliffs exceed 100 feet in many places, and weak shale-beds can be seen to alternate with Liassic limestone bands. Wave erosion is very active, and the *wave-cut platform* at the foot of the cliff is over a quarter of a mile wide. Such platforms at the foot of cliffs are common all around the coasts of Wales, good examples occurring also at Southerndown, Glamorgan, in Gower (*e.g.* on the south side of the Mumbles Head near Swansea (153, 6387)) and in Pembrokeshire, for example, in the bay of Freshwater West (151, 8899 and 8898).

In the Aberystwyth–Aberaeron section of the Cardiganshire coast an interesting series of low cliffs has been cut into boulder clay which (as south of Harlech and again near Rhyl and Prestatyn) has been piled up against the land margin by the Irish Sea ice from Cardigan Bay (p. 75). This boulder clay forms coastal platforms of 50–60 feet O.D. which are best developed seaward of the road A487 between Llansantffraid (127, 5167) and Llanrhystyd (5369), but which are being removed by wave action at a perceptible rate (Figs. 102 and 103). These cliffs are steep and well gullied, and

FIG. 102.   Undercutting of a boulder-clay cliff between Aberarth and Llanon, Cardiganshire.

FIG. 103. Boulder-clay cliffs between Aberystwyth and Llanrhystyd, Cardiganshire. The cliffs are being undermined and rapidly demolished by wave action, the larger pebbles and boulders being left on the beach.

owe their form to rapid undercutting, slumping and collapse rather than resistance to wave action. The foreshore of the boulder-clay section of cliffs is composed of shingle with a few strewn boulders, *e.g.* west of Llansantffraid or near Morfa Bychan (5677), but elsewhere along this section of coast, wave-cut platforms have been eroded in a solid cliff, 300–350 feet O.D.

Illustration of the interesting relationships between folding, faulting and jointing of rocks and sea erosion is given in the general form of the cliffs in the Tenby Peninsula and in Gower, though, as elsewhere, the details depend upon a variety of other factors. The south coast of both peninsulas follows the line of the east–west (Hercynian) trend of the rock outcrop, whereas their east and west coasts cut across the outcrops. Between Linney Head (151, 883958) and Stackpole (996942) in the Tenby Peninsula, the Carboniferous Limestone presents a broad front to the ceaseless attack of the waves, and the almost vertical cliffs, 100–160 feet high, might justly be claimed to be the most striking limestone cliffs in Britain (Fig. 108). The character of the rock is such that the cliffs have been cut into a variety of forms by not only direct sea action but by chemical weathering by rainwater charged with carbon dioxide and by normal sub-aerial denudation. Much the same applies to the Great Orme

K

Fig. 104. Cormorant Rock, or Craig-y-Filfran, a sea-stack north of Aberystwyth.

Fig. 105. The 'Green Bridge' of Wales, south of Warren, Pembrokeshire. A natural arch in Carboniferous Limestone.

FIG. 106. Ancient sea-stacks of intrusive igneous rock protruding above a marine platform cut across a variety of sedimentary strata. West Pembrokeshire near St. David's.

Headland, Llandudno (Fig. 61), which is also composed of Carboniferous Limestone.

Sea erosion along joints, faults and planes of weakness in rocky cliff-faces has been responsible for many slit-like caves, and, where these have collapsed, long, narrow inlets are formed. The famous Huntsman's Leap (151, 965928) in Pembrokeshire is a good example of such an inlet. Elsewhere fragments will remain on the foreshore in the form of *stacks*, Cormorant Rock or Craig-y-Filfran (Fig. 104) north of Aberystwyth (127, 583830) being a fine instance. These may sometimes be connected to the mainland by a rock bridge or natural arch, as in the 'Green Bridge' of Wales, south of Warren in Pembrokeshire (Fig. 105), which will ultimately fall under the continued attack of the waves, leaving an isolated stack. This also must disappear. The small, isolated hillocks of igneous rocks (*e.g.* Carn Llidi (138 or 151, 7328), and Penbiri (7629) protruding above the flat plateau-tops of western Pembrokeshire (Fig. 106)), may be regarded as old sea-stacks which were left as the surrounding marine platforms were cut back and which have maintained themselves above the general level by virtue of their superior resistance to sub-aerial and marine denudation.

Finally, mention should be made of the pronounced effect that angle of dip of the rock strata has on the form of any cliff. When the strata are tilted backwards and inland away from the sea, cliffs tend to have steep faces. Fig. 107 shows such cliffs carved out of highly inclined beds of Carboniferous Limestone along the south coast of Gower. The marine platform inland is clearly visible in this view. Horizontally stratified rocks tend to give much the same kind of cliff, but where the strata dip towards the sea there is always the tendency for blocks of rock to break off along joints (which lie at right-angles to the planes of stratification) and slope away from the land margin into the sea to form a cliff with a sloping face. The view near Castlemartin, Pembrokeshire (Fig. 108), shows such a cliff, with, in right centre, the sloping profile after the rocks have broken off, and, in the foreground, a well-jointed section which in due time will undoubtedly slip away into the sea. Note the sea-stack in the background.

Storm Beaches.—These familiar features along our coasts all show a characteristic high ridge of pebbles with a step-like profile that results from the tendency of the waves, especially during a gale, to drive the largest pebbles forward and to drag only the smaller ones and sand back seawards. The edge of each terrace, the section

Fig. 107. Cliffs carved in Carboniferous Limestone with strata tilted landwards, Rhosili, Gower, Glamorgan.

FIG. 108. Cliffs in Carboniferous Limestone, Castlemartin, Pembrokeshire. The seaward tilt of the strata causes sections of the cliff-face to
break off. Note also the even skyline of the 200-foot coastal platform.

FIG. 109. A storm beach at Cold Knap, Barry, Glamorgan. The eastward drift of pebbles along the shore (*left*) is arrested by the headland
of Carboniferous Limestone in the foreground.

FIG. 110. Storm beach at Aberaeron, showing evidence of
scalloping after heavy storm of 3rd February 1957.

which is subject to continual change, is determined by the height of the tide and the force of the winds responsible for its formation

In the case of the storm beach at Cold Knap, Barry, Glamorgan (Fig. 109), one of the finest of its kind in the country, investigation has shown that the pebbles, derived from the Liassic limestones of the cliffs to the west, drift eastwards along the shore until they are arrested by what can be regarded as a 'natural groyne' of Carboniferous Limestone, *i.e.* the headland projecting at the eastern end of the beach. Waves of reflection, in fact, move material back westwards off this headland by as much as 50 feet. Close examination of the beach itself shows a series of beach cusps running into the sea roughly at right-angles; these owe their origin, in part, to the extraordinarily high tidal range experienced in the Bristol Channel. At Portishead, Somerset, on the south shore of the Bristol Channel, the highest tidal range is 42 feet. This fluctuation is exceeded only by that in the Bay of Fundy of eastern Canada, where the 44·2-foot tidal range at Noel Bay is the highest in the world.

Other good examples of storm beaches are to be found at Tanybwlch (127, 5780), Aberaeron (139, 4563, Fig. 110) and Borth (127, 6089), all on the coast of Cardigan Bay. In each case much of the material of which they are constructed has been contributed by the deposits of boulder clay banked up against the Cardigan Bay coast by the Irish Sea ice (p. 75). Equally characteristic is the storm beach at Newgale, Pembroke (151, 8422).

Dunes.—Between Abergele and the Clwyd Estuary, in Newborough Warren and Morfa Dinlle in North Wales, at Morfa Harlech, Morfa Dyffryn, Fairbourne and Ynyslas on the Cardigan Bay coast, and at places such as Laugharne, Pembrey, Whiteford, Aberavon, Kenfig and Merthyr Mawr in South Wales, there are several large *sand-dune* areas. Wide foreshores, exposed at low tide, provide the necessary sand which dries out quickly and is soon set in motion by the wind. If the wind is from the sea towards the land, the sand soon encroaches on the land, unless wet ground, vegetation or some obstacle arrests it and causes it to start to accumulate. A covering of vegetation will fix the dunes, but if the vegetation is disturbed at any point, there is a local increase in the rate of sand movement, with the formation of a small gap which gets bigger and a *blow-out* is formed. Blow-outs are a common feature in the sand dunes of Kenfig Burrows near Port Talbot, Glamorgan (Fig. 111). In the absence of adequate stabilisation the

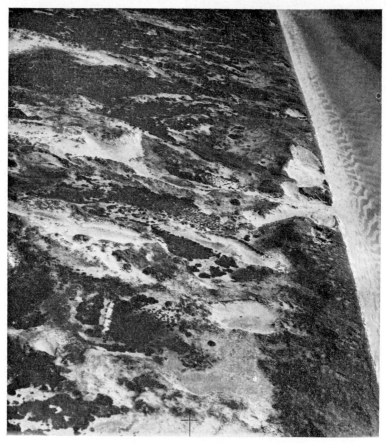

Fig. 111. Sand dunes and blow-outs at Kenfig Burrows,
near Port Talbot, Glamorgan.

dunes at Whiteford Burrows (152, 4495) on the south side of the
Loughor estuary have advanced about one and a half miles into the
estuary. At Llandanwg (116, 569284) in Merioneth the church has
been almost completely overwhelmed (Fig. 112), though some of
the gravestones were installed as recently as 1860 and 1870.

Newborough Warren (Fig. 113) in Anglesey is a particularly fine
example of a dune area. It probably derived its sand, in the first
instance, from glacial debris which accumulated along the margins
of the Quaternary ice-sheets. Ice from the Clyde and southern
Uplands of Scotland, from the Lake District and from the heights
of north-eastern Ireland, descended and converged into the de-

pression of the Irish Sea (p. 75). From this area of congestion, the combined flows moved southwards under great pressure pushing and scraping debris before them. A western limb of this ice and associated mud, sand and gravels, thrust against, and over-rode, Anglesey. The debris from this ice-lobe was transported by rivers and deposited near the coasts of Caernarvon Bay, then washed up on to the beaches by marine action and was removed inland by the prevailing south-westerly winds. The dunes are encroaching on good agricultural land, but are being progressively fixed by marram and other coarse grasses and trees.

In South Wales the evidence of the dune areas points to a period of stability up to the early part of the thirteenth century, but a period of storminess in the fourteenth century brought about a comparatively sudden change and sand did great damage to property and cultivated land. The sand dunes at Kenfig Burrows (153, 7981) rest upon Keuper Marls and other rocks of Triassic and Carboniferous age. No advance of the dunes seems to have taken place here until at least the close of the twelfth century (Higgins, 1933) as the castle (801827) was known to have been occupied in 1152, and in 1184 the port was still in use. The 'Via Julia', which passed through the north-east corner of the region was, nevertheless, open

FIG. 112. Encroachment by sand, Llandanwg Church, near Harlech, Merioneth.   Gravestones as recent as 1870 have been covered.

FIG. 113. Sand dunes at Newborough Warren, Anglesey.

in 1344, but by 1485 was being gradually covered by sand. Although the inner margin has been fixed by a plant cover, sand blown out from the dunes continues to trouble residents of recently constructed housing estates at Cornelly. The evidence of the dunes at Merthyr Mawr Warren (153, 8676) similarly points to fixation and stabilisation during the Norman period, followed by a renewed onset of sand migration, which finally reached even the top of the limestone scarp to the north. The dunes have achieved heights of over 200 feet and, apart from those of East Prussia, are the tallest in Europe.

APPENDIX I

'One-Inch' Ordnance Survey Sheets of Wales
Seventh Series

Sheet Number

106	Anglesey
107	Snowdon
108	Denbigh
*109	Chester
115	Pwllheli
116	Dolgelley
117	Bala and Welshpool
*118	Shrewsbury
127	Aberystwyth
128	Montgomery and Llandrindod Wells
*129	Ludlow
138	Fishguard
139	Cardigan
140	Llandovery
141	Brecon
*142	Hereford
151	Pembroke
152	Carmarthen and Tenby
153	Swansea
154	Cardiff
155	Bristol and Newport

Note.—Sheets marked * cover largely English territory, with only relatively small areas of Wales.

APPENDIX II

Summary Landform Table

LANDFORM	WELSH EXAMPLE	OTHER BRITISH EXAMPLES
TECTONIC FEATURES		
Fault-guided valley	Tal-y-llyn valley, Merioneth	Glen More, Scotland
Rift valley	Dyffryn Clwyd, Denbigh	Central Valley of Scotland
Fault-line escarpment	Western edge of Conway valley (Dolgarrog), Caernarvon	Western face of North Pennines overlocking Eden valley
Anticline	Teifi anticline (denuded), Cardigan–Carmarthen	Weald (denuded)
Syncline	Caerphilly basin, Glamorgan	London basin
IGNEOUS FEATURES		
Lava flow	Tryfan (Ordovician), Caernarvon	Antrim plateau (Tertiary)
Sill	Cadair Idris escarpment, Merioneth	Great Whin Sill, Northumberland; Salisbury Crags, Edinburgh
Dyke	Porth Colman, Llŷn, Caernarvon	Cleveland dyke, north-east Yorkshire
Volcanic plug	Yr Eifl, Llŷn, Caernarvon	Bass Rock; Castle Rock, Edinburgh; North Berwick Law; Inchcape Rock
GRADATIONAL FEATURES		
FLUVIAL FEATURES		
Young river valley	Upper tributaries of Tywi, Carmarthen	Feature of most upland areas in Britain
Mature river valley	Severn valley, near Welshpool, Montgomery	Cuckmere valley, near Westdean, Sussex, and lower reaches of most river valleys
Old river valley	Lower Dee valley, Denbigh–Flint	Lower Severn

LANDFORM	WELSH EXAMPLE	OTHER BRITISH EXAMPLES
Polycyclic relief	Interior Cardigan	Common in Britain since effects of late Tertiary movements of uplift are widespread
River terraces	River Dyfi between Cemmaes and Mallwyd, Montgomery.	River Thames near London
Incised meanders	Middle Rheidol, Cardigan	Wye below Ross; Wear at Durham
River capture	Bargoed Taff by Taff, Glamorgan	Blyth and Wansbeck by N. Tyne, Northumberland Darent by Medway, Kent
Escarpment	Black Mountains, Brecon	South Downs; Lincoln Cliff; Chiltern and Cotswold scarps
Superimposed drainage	Rivers in south-east Wales	Rivers of Lake District, (Cumbrian Mts.)
Gorge	Taff's Well (superimposed drainage), Glamorgan	Ironbridge, Salop (glacial overflow channel); Cheddar (limestone); Tyne Gap; Goring Gap
Cefn (Hog's Back)	Caerphilly Mountain, Glamorgan	Hog's Back, Guildford
Limestone (karst) scenery	Minera–Llangollen district, Denbigh	Peak District, Derby; Ingleborough, W. Riding of Yorks.

GLACIAL FEATURES

Glaciated valley	Nant Ffrancon, Caernarvon	Great Langdale valley in English Lake District
Hanging valley	Cwm Ceunant, Nant Ffrancon, Caernarvon	Lodore Falls near Keswick
Ribbon Lake	Llyn Padarn, Caernarvon	Windermere and Ennerdale, English Lake District
Blaen (trough's end)	Blaen Rhondda, Glamorgan	Mickleden (head of Great Langdale valley), Westmorland
Cirque (corrie)	Llyn Dulyn (Carneddau), Caernarvon	Lochnagar, Aberdeen; Blea Water, above Mardale, English Lake District
Crib (arête)	Crib Goch, Caernarvon	Striding Edge, Helvellyn

LANDFORM	WELSH EXAMPLE	OTHER BRITISH EXAMPLES
Glaciated plateau	Migneint, Merioneth	Western Isles, Scotland
Marginal lake	Lake Teifi, Cardigan	'Lake Harrison', south-east Midlands between Stratford and Leicester
Overflow channel	Dinas valley (near Dinas Head) Pembroke	Forge Gap and Malton Gap (River Derwent, Yorks.)
Moraine	Glais, near Swansea, Glamorgan	East-west belt across Central Cheshire
Drumlins	Hirwaun district, Glamorgan	Lough Neagh district, Northern Ireland; Central Valley of Scotland; Solway Plain, coast of Morecambe Bay, near Lancaster

COASTAL FEATURES

Ria	Milford Haven, Pembroke	Carrick Roads (Falmouth); Bantry and Dingle Bays, south-west Ireland
Sandspit	Fairbourne, Merioneth	Gt. Yarmouth; Calshot (Southampton Water); Hurst Castle; Orford Ness
Marine platform	200-foot platform in Vale of Glamorgan	200-foot platform on Downs of south-eastern England
Storm beach	Cold Knap, Barry, Glamorgan	Chesil Bank, Weymouth
Sand dunes	Kenfig Burrows, Merthyr Mawr Warren, Glamorgan	Dawlish Warren; Culbin Sands, Nairn and Moray; Blakeney Point, Norfolk

APPENDIX III

The Principal Classes of Rock

THE simplest and most common classification of rock types is that based upon their origin. In this way, three types may be distinguished although there may be some over-lapping between categories 2 and 3.

1. *Igneous Rocks* are rocks which (derived from masses of deep-seated lava or *magma*) have solidified from the molten state. They may solidify after having poured out on to the earth's surface (*extrusions*), or if the original lava fails to reach the surface the solidification takes place underground (*intrusions*). Many of the igneous rocks of Wales were extruded on to the sea-bed in Ordovician times; in this case they became covered by sedimentary deposition (see below). These *contemporaneous* igneous rocks, however, resemble intrusions in that they may not have been finally exposed at the surface until they were contorted by earth-movements and the overlying sediments stripped away by the forces of weathering and erosion (p. 20).

2. *Sedimentary Rocks* result from the deposition of non-soluble particles in water by gravitation. Such deposition is greatest in seas where material brought in by rivers and eroded by waves from the coasts is distributed over the sea-floor, where it accumulates over long-continued periods of geological time. Generally speaking, the coarsest particles are deposited near the shore, while the finest particles are often carried to the deepest water. Continuous accumulation of this kind eventually leads to the formation of *strata* of sedimentary rocks. Initially horizontal, these strata are usually distorted to greater or lesser degree by earth-movements (p. 1) which take place subsequent to their formation. Older sediments are often intensely folded in extremely complex patterns (Fig. 3).

Soluble material may also be deposited on the floors of seas or lakes by precipitation as the water becomes over-saturated. Examples are rock salt and gypsum. Most limestones result from the secretions of marine organisms. Neither of these types of rock is sedimentary within the strict definition of the term; they are, nevertheless, often regarded as such since they show pronounced stratification as do the true sedimentaries.

Since the geological circumstances of seas change from time to time, it is usual to find a succession of beds of varying sedimentary material one above the other. Where there is a marked variation in durability between these successive beds, tilting and subsequent *differential* (p. 61) erosion may emphasise the relief of the more resistant beds.   In general, the age of rocks increases with present depth, but there may be local exceptions due to over-thrusting (p. 2).

3. *Metamorphic Rocks* have been transformed from pre-existing rocks by processes of change, the commonest causes being pressure caused by earth-movements and the heat associated with igneous activity.   This transformation, however, must have been sufficiently thorough to produce a well-defined, new rock type with important properties of its own distinct from those of the original formation.

Many rocks which were initially sedimentary have undergone metamorphosis of this kind.   Hence slate is derived from shale in the first instance, but during the process has acquired properties of its own, in particular, that of being fissile into thin sheets along planes independent of the original bedding.   Marble was produced by the metamorphosis of limestone, but it has the additional property of being able to take a polish.

The evolution of the present rock-forms of the earth's crust is thus a consequence of two principal classes of forces:

(i) Rock *formation*, including the accumulation of successions of beds of varying sediments, the metamorphosis of these sediments, and the interference of intrusions and extrusions of masses of originally deep-seated lava.

(ii) Rock *deformations*, produced during periodic outbursts of crustal instability which have contorted and distorted the strata resulting from (i), and which have themselves caused further metamorphosis.

The relation of the succession of rock formation to the three principal spasms of earth-movements is shown in the accompanying table.

L

Era	System	Approximate Date of Commencement of System in Millions of Years	Climate
QUATERNARY	RECENT	$\frac{1}{4}$	TEMPERATE
	PLEISTOCENE	I	GLACIAL
TERTIARY	PLIOCENE	15	COOLING
	MIOCENE	35	
	OLIGOCENE	50	TEMPERATE
	EOCENE	70	
MESOZOIC	CRETACEOUS	120	PROBABLY WARM
	JURASSIC	150	
	RHAETIC	160	
	TRIASSIC	190	DRY
UPPER PALAEOZOIC	PERMIAN	220	DRY
	CARBONIFEROUS	280	WARM, HUM
	DEVONIAN (OLD RED SANDSTONE)	320	DRY
LOWER PALAEOZOIC	SILURIAN	350	
	ORDOVICIAN	400	WARM
	CAMBRIAN	500	
PRE-CAMBRIAN		PROBABLY OVER 4,000	PROBABLY EVERY CLIM ATIC TYPE

BLE

Kind of Rock in Wales	Major Episodes in Geological History of Wales
ver alluvium, sands and soils	Slight oscillations of sea-level
acial sand, gravels, silts, boulder clay	Ice Age
	ALPINE (TERTIARY) EARTH-MOVEMENTS. Only slight movements in Wales
ales and limestones	Possible transgression of late Mesozoic seas over whole of Wales Minor transgression of early Mesozoic seas into the borders of Wales
nglomerates, sandstones and marls (in Mon. and Glam.)	Desert conditions following mountain building and uplift
	HERCYNIAN (ARMORICAN) EARTH - MOVEMENTS. Development of E.–W. structures in South Wales
ales, sandstones and coals. Grits and sandstones. Limestones	Widespread swamps and deltas in South with formation of coals
ddish sandstones and marls	Widespread desert conditions after mountain building and uplift
ales, sandstones in west, limestones in east	CALEDONIAN EARTH-MOVEMENTS producing the main structural trends (N.N.E.-S.S.W.) in North and Central Wales
ales and sandstones, with volcanic ashes and lava	
ales, sandstones and grits	Geosynclinal sedimentation with widespread volcanic activity during the Ordovician
most wholly igneous and metamorphic rocks	Rocks of this age occur in Anglesey, south-west Llŷn and parts of W. Pembrokeshire and were greatly deformed by earth-movements before the deposition of Cambrian sediments

Bibliography

1. General Textbooks and Works of Reference

British Regional Geology: North Wales, London, H.M.S.O., 1961.
British Regional Geology: South Wales, London, H.M.S.O., 1948.
British Regional Geology: The Welsh Borderland, London, H.M.S.O., 1948.
Brown, E. H. *The Relief and Drainage of Wales*, Cardiff, University of Wales Press, 1960.
Cotton, C. A. *Geomorphology*, 3rd edition, Christchurch, Whitcombe and Tombs, 1942.
Landscape as developed by Processes of Normal Erosion, 2nd edition, London, Cambridge University Press, 1949.
Dury, G. H. *The Face of the Earth*, Harmondsworth, Penguin Books, 1959.
Holmes, A. *Principles of Physical Geology*, London, Nelson, 1944.
Horrocks, N. K. *Physical Geography and Climatology*, London, Longmans, Green, 1953.
Lake, P. *Physical Geography*, 4th edition, London, Cambridge University Press, 1958.
Monkhouse, F. J. *The Principles of Physical Geography*, 3rd edition, London, University of London Press, 1957.
North, F. J., *et alii*. *Snowdonia*, London, Collins (New Naturalist Series), 1949.
Sparks, B. W. *Geomorphology*, London, Longmans, Green, 1960.
Stamp, L. D. *Britain's Structure and Scenery*, London, Collins (New Naturalist Series), 1946.
Steers, J. A. *The Coastline of England and Wales*, London, Cambridge University Press, 1946.
Trueman, A. E. *Geology and Scenery of England and Wales*, London, V. Gollancz, 1938; Harmondsworth, Penguin Books, 1949.
Wooldridge, S. W., & Morgan, R. S. *An Outline of Geomorphology*, London, Longmans, Green, 1959.

2. Other Works and Papers referred to

Brown, E. H. 1952. 'The River Ystwyth, Cardiganshire: a geomorphological analysis', *Proc. Geol. Assoc.*, vol. 63, p. 244.
1957(a). 'The 600-foot platform in Wales', *Proc. VIIIth Gen. Assembly and XVIIth Congress Int. Geog. Union, Washington.*
1957(b). 'The physique of Wales', *Geog. Journ.*, vol. 123, p. 208.

Challinor, J. 1930. 'The hill-top surface of North Cardiganshire', *Geography*, vol. 15, p. 651.
Charlesworth, J. K. 1929. 'The South Wales end-moraine', *Quart. Journ. Geol. Soc.*, vol. 85, p. 335.
Embleton, C. 1961. 'The geomorphology of the Vale of Conway, North Wales, with particular reference to its deglaciation', *Trans. Inst. Brit. Geog.*, no. 29, p. 47.
George, T. N. 1942. 'The development of the Towy and Upper Usk drainage pattern', *Quart. Journ. Geol. Soc.*, vol. 98, p. 89.
Godwin, H., & Mitchell, G. F. 1938. 'Stratigraphy and development of two raised bogs near Tregaron, Cardiganshire', *New Phytologist*, vol. 37, p. 425.
Green, J. F. N. 1936. 'The terraces of southernmost England', *Quart. Journ. Geol. Soc.*, vol. 92, lxviii.
Greenly, E. 1919. 'The geology of Anglesey', *Memoir of the Geological Survey*.
Griffiths, J. C. 1940. 'The glacial deposits west of the Taff, South Wales', unpublished Ph.D. thesis, London University (Imp. Coll. Sci.).
Harker, A. 1889. 'The Bala volcanic series of Caernarvonshire and associated rocks', Cambridge University Press.
Higgins, L. S. 1933. 'An investigation into the problem of the sand-dune areas on the South Wales coast', *Arch. Camb.*, June 1933, p. 26.
Howe, G. M., & Yates, R. A. 1953. 'A bathymetrical study of Llyn Cau', *Geography*, vol. 38, p. 124.
Jehu, T. J. 1902. 'A bathymetrical and geological study of the lakes of Snowdonia and East Caernarvonshire', *Trans. Royal Soc. Edinburgh*, vol. 40, p. 419.
Jones, O. T. 1951. 'The drainage systems of Wales and the adjacent regions', *Quart. Journ. Geol. Soc.*, vol. 107, p. 201.
Jones, R. O. 1939. 'The evolution of the Neath–Tawe drainage', *Proc. Geol. Assoc.*, vol. 66, p. 247.
Linton, D. L. 1951. 'The Midland drainage', *The Advancement of Science*, vol. 7, p. 449.
North, F. J. 1957. 'Sunken cities', Cardiff, University of Wales Press.
Strahan, A. 1902. 'On the origins of the river system of South Wales and its connection with the Thames', *Quart. Journ. Geol. Soc.*, vol. 58, p. 207.
     1907. 'The geology of the Swansea district', *Memoir of the Geological Survey*.
Watson, E. G. 1960. 'Glacial landforms in the Cadair Idris area', *Geography*, vol. 45, p. 27.
     1962. 'The glacial morphology of the Tal-y-llyn valley', *Trans. Inst. Brit. Geog.*, no. 30, p. 15.
Wills, L. J. 1912. 'Late glacial and post-glacial changes in the lower Dee Valley', *Quart. Journ. Geol. Soc.*, vol. 68, p. 180.

Index

Figures in heavy type are the pages on which the specific landform
or subject is described, and, where possible, explained

Mynydd Drumau, 10
Mynydd Drws-y-Coed, 89
Mynydd Epynt, xiv, xvi, 91
Mynydd Llangatwg, 71
Mynydd Llangynidr, 69, 71
Mynydd March-Hywel, 10
Mynydd Mawr, 28
Mynydd Mwyn Mawr erratic, 102
Mynydd Perfedd, 28
Mynydd Prescelly, xiv, xvi, 121
Mynydd Sylen, 122
Mynydd Tal-y-Mignedd, 89

Nant Bwa Drain, 80, 81
Nant Cawrddu, 82
Nant Ffrancon, 78, 79, 80
Nant Graig Wen, 82
Nant Llechog, 82
Nant-y-Bugail, 96
Natural arch, 128
Neath, Vale of, xiv, 7
Neath (Nedd), river, 59
  valley, 56, 78
Negative movements, 2, 44
Nevern marginal lake, 95
Newborough Warren, 133, 134, 135, 136
Normal fault, 3, 4

Ogmore river, 66
Old-age valleys, **41**
Old landscape, 31
Oligocene period, 144
Ordovician period, 144
Orogenetic movements, 2
Overflow channels, 75, **93**
Ox-bow lake, 41, 42

Padarn ridge, xiv, 28
Palaeozoic period, Lower, 144
  Upper, 144
Parson's Bridge, 48
Patella beach, 124
Paviland caves, 124
Penbiri, 129
Peneplain, 45
Penmaen Mawr, 28
Pen Pleidian, 26
Pentre Dolamarch, 43
Pentyrch platform, 120, 121
Pen-y-Gadair, 25
Permian period, 144
Pirate stream, 53
Pleistocene period, 144

Pliocene period, 144
Plunge, 113
Plynlimon, xvi, 73
Polycyclic relief, **44**
Pont ar Elan, 49
Pontrhydygroes, 59
Pontsticill, 70
Pontypridd anticline, xiv
Porth-yr-Ogof, 71
Positive movements, 2
Pot-holes, 35, 36
Pre-Cambrian period, 144
Proto-Dee river, 58
Prysor river, 48
Pwll Glas, 36
Pyg Track, 17

Quaternary period, xvii, 144

Radial drainage, 55
Radnor Forest, xvi, 73, 91
Raised beaches, 124
Recent period, 144
Recessional moraines, 98, 99
Recumbent Folds, 2
Rejuvenation, 2, 32, 50, 107
Reverse fault, 3, 4
Rhaeadr Ogwen, 78
Rhaeadr-y-Cwm, 46
Rhaetic period, 144
Rheidol, falls, 59
  river, 38, 48, 60, 81
Rhinog Mountains, 17, 73
Rhiw-yr-Ysgyfarnog, 89
Rhobell Fawr, 19
Rhos Dirion, 61
Rhosili cliffs, 130
Rhydding fault, 10
Rhydymwyn elbow of capture, 59
Rhymni river, 42, 56, 66
Rhyolites, 21
Rias, 110
Ribbon lakes, 76, 77, **82**
Ridgeway anticline, xiv
Rift valleys, **8**
Ritec fault, xiv
River, capture, **52**
  terraces, **49**
Roches moutonnées, **91**
Rock basins, 76, 82
Ruabon Mountain, 70

St. David's Head, 26
St. David's platform, 123
Sand dunes, **133**

THE END

PRINTED BY R. & R. CLARK, LTD., EDINBURGH